F. G. J. Norton has published successful textbooks at both A and O level. He is the author of *Advanced Level Applied Mathematics*, and co-author with L. Harwood Clarke of *Additional Applied Mathematics*, *Additional Pure Mathematics*, *Pure Mathematics at Advanced Level* and *O-level Mathematics*. He is also the author of *Advanced Mathematics* in the Pan Study Aids series.

Mr Norton has been an examiner for the London and Cambridge boards and chief examiner in Mathematics for the Associated Examining Boards. He was until recently Head of Mathematics at Rugby School.

Pan Study Aids for GCSE include:

Accounting

Biology

Chemistry

Commerce

Computer Studies

Economics

English Language

French

Geography 1

Geography 2

German

History 1: World History since 1914

History 2: Britain and Europe since 1700

Human Biology

Mathematics

Physics

Sociology

Study Skills

PAN STUDY AIDS

MATHEMATICS

F. G. J. Norton

A Pan Original

Pan Books   London, Sydney and Auckland

First published 1987 by Pan Books Ltd,
Cavaye Place, London SW10 9PG

9 8 7 6 5 4 3

© F. G. J. Norton 1987

ISBN 0 330 29941 7

Text design by Peter Ward
Text illustrations by M L Design
Photoset by Parker Typesetting Service, Leicester
Printed and bound in Spain by
Mateu Cromo, SA Madrid

CONTENTS

Introduction to GCSE   8
Preface   10
Introduction   11
General examination hints   22

1 ▶ **Arithmetic**   23

2 ▶ **Fractions and decimals; percentages**   31

3 ▶ **Indices; numbers in standard form**   39

4 ▶ **Efficient use of the calculator**   47

5 ▶ **Ratio and percentage; taxes**   55

6 ▶ **Simple and compound interest**   65

7 ▶ **Units; area and volume; similarity; accuracy**   71

8 ▶ **Estimation and approximation**   79

9 ▶ **Statistics and the representation of data**   85

10 ▶ **Probability**   97

Contents

11 ▶ Algebra 105

12 ▶ Algebra: equations and inequalities 115

13 ▶ Straight-line graphs 127

14 ▶ Graphs 139

15 ▶ Inequalities: graphical representation, linear programming 153

16 ▶ Geometry: parallel lines, triangles, isometry, quadrilaterals 165

17 ▶ Commonly used theorems 177

18 ▶ Loci and constructions 191

19 ▶ Nets of solids 199

20 ▶ Trigonometry: definitions, right-angled triangles 205

21 ▶ Sine and cosine formulae; three-dimensional problems 217

22 ▶ Sets and set notation 229

23 ▶ **Relations and functions** 235

24 ▶ **Matrices** 241

25 ▶ **Geometrical applications of matrices** 253

26 ▶ **Vectors** 265

27 ▶ **Flow charts** 277

28 ▶ **Iterative methods to solve equations** 289

Answers 295

Index 311

INTRODUCTION TO GCSE

From 1988, there will be a single system of examining at 16 plus in England, Wales and Northern Ireland. The General Certificate of Secondary Education (GCSE) will replace the General Certificate of Education (GCE) and the Certificate of Secondary Education (CSE). In Scotland candidates will be entering for the O grade and standard grade examinations leading to the award of the Scottish Certificate of Education (SCE).

The Pan Study Aids GCSE series has been specially written by practising teachers and examiners to enable you to prepare successfully for this new examination.

GCSE introduces several important changes in the way in which you are tested. First, the examinations will be structured so that you can show *what* you know rather than what you do *not* know. Of critical importance here is the work you produce during the course of the examination year, which will be given much greater emphasis than before. Second, courses are set and marked by six examining groups instead of the previous twenty GCE/CSE boards. The groups are:

Northern Examining Association (NEA)
Midland Examining Group (MEG)
London and East Anglian Group (LEAG)
Southern Examining Group (SEG)
Welsh Joint Examinations Council (WJEC)
Northern Ireland Schools Examination Council (NISEC)

One of the most useful changes introduced by GCSE is the single award system of grades A–G. This should permit you and future employers to assess more accurately your qualifications.

GCSE	GCE O Level	CSE
A	A	–
B	B	–
C	C	1
D	D	2
E	E	3
F	F	4
G		5

Remember that, whatever examinations you take, the grades you are awarded will be based on how well you have done.

Pan Study Aids are geared for use throughout the duration of your courses. The text layout has been carefully designed to provide all the information and skills you need for GCSE and SCE examinations – please feel free to use the margins for additional notes.

PREFACE

In May 1988 the General Certificate of Secondary Education (GCSE) will be introduced in all schools and colleges in England, Wales and Northern Ireland. It will supersede the General Certificate of Education (GCE) and the Certificate of Secondary Education (CSE), though these examinations have been gradually replaced by 'joint schemes' in the immediately preceding years. The new examination will be administered by examining groups, whose names and addresses are given on pages 11–15, and which replace the examining boards that had administered the earlier examinations.

The nature of the examination in mathematics is likely to change considerably in the early years, and candidates should consult up-to-date syllabuses to augment the summaries given on pages 18–21. The school-based assessment part will become compulsory in 1991, at which stage aural and oral testing will also be introduced. The number of marks available for the written examination will be reduced, and candidates should check with their schools exactly what will be required of them when they take the examination.

Candidates should also check the level at which they are entering for the examination. Many of the topics are tested by easy questions at one level, harder questions at the next level, and then finally harder questions still at the hardest level. Those candidates taking the examination at a lower level therefore do not need to cover all the work on such topics, and they should judge the difficulty of questions they can be asked by use of the specimen papers and past papers.

I should like to thank the examining groups for permission to reproduce questions from their specimen papers; the answers given are my own. I should also like to thank all at Pan Books for their help and unfailing courtesy during the production of this book.

Rugby 1987   F. G. J. Norton

INTRODUCTION

THE EXAMINING GROUPS

The examining groups conducting the examination are as follows.

▶ The **London and East Anglian Group for GCSE** (LEAG), comprising:

East Anglian Examination Board
The Lindens
Lexden Road
Colchester
Essex CO3 3RL

London Regional Examining Board
Lyon House
104 Wandsworth High Street
London SW18 4LF

University of London Schools Examination Board
Stewart House
32 Russell Square
London WC1B 5DN

▶ The **Midland Examining Group** (MEG), comprising:

East Midland Regional Examinations Board
Robins Wood House
Robins Wood Road
Aspley
Nottingham NG8 3NR

Oxford and Cambridge Schools Examination Board
10 Trumpington Street
Cambridge CB2 1QB
and
Elsfield Way
Oxford OX2 8EP

Southern Universities Joint Board for Schools Examinations
Cotham Road
Bristol BS6 6DD

The West Midlands Examinations Board
Norfolk House
Smallbrook Queensway
Birmingham B5 4NJ

University of Cambridge Local Examinations Syndicate
Syndicate Buildings
1 Hills Road
Cambridge

♦ The **Northern Examining Association** (NEA), comprising:

Associated Lancashire Schools Examining Board
12 Harter Street
Manchester M1 6HL

Joint Matriculation Board
Manchester M15 6EU

North Regional Examinations Board
Wheatfield Road
Westerhope
Newcastle-upon-Tyne NE5 5JZ

North West Regional Examinations Board
Orbit House
Albert Street
Eccles
Manchester M30 0WL

Yorkshire and Humberside Regional Examinations Board
Harrogate Office
31–3 Springfield Avenue
Harrogate HG1 2HW
and
Sheffield Office
Scarsdale House
136 Derbyshire Lane
Sheffield S8 8SE

♦ The **Southern Examining Group** (SEG), comprising:

The South East Regional Examinations Board
Beloe House
2/10 Mount Ephraim Road
Tunbridge Wells
Kent TN1 1EU

The Associated Examining Board
Stag Hill House
Guildford
Surrey GU2 5XJ

The Southern Regional Examinations Board
Avondale House
33 Carlton Crescent
Southampton
Hants SO9 4YL

Oxford Delegacy for Local Examinations
Ewert Place
Banbury Road
Summertown
Oxford OX2 7BZ

South Western Examinations Board
23/29 Marsh Street
Bristol BS1 4BP

▶ In **Wales** the examination is administered by:

Welsh Joint Education Committee (WJEC)
245 Western Avenue
Cardiff CF5 2YX

▶ and in **Northern Ireland** by:

Northern Ireland Schools Examination Council (NISEC)
Beechill House
42 Beechill Road
Belfast BT8 4RS

Each examining group has its own syllabus (mode 1), and often an 'SMP-type' syllabus, as well as syllabuses for other projects and for groups of schools and colleges. Check with your own school which syllabus you are taking. Syllabuses and details of the entry procedure can be obtained from the appropriate board; the syllabuses are augmented by most helpful notes and explanations.

LEVEL OF EXAMINATION

In mathematics there are usually three levels of examinations, the difficulty of the examination being determined by the syllabus and by the standard of question asked on each part of the syllabus. The grades available in the examination are determined by the level at which the candidate enters the examination (see Table 1). It is not in your advantage to enter for too high a level, as candidates scoring below the marks required for the lowest grade awarded at each level are unclassified; it may well be better to try and enter at, say, the Intermediate level of the Midland Examining Group and obtain a grade E rather than to enter at the Higher level of that board and to be unclassified.

Table 1: Levels of examination of the various boards

Board	Levels available	Grades awarded
LEAG	X Y Z	E F G C D E F A B C D
MEG	Foundation Intermediate Higher	E F G C D E F A B C D
NEA	P Q R	E F G C D E F A B C D
SEG	1 2 3	E F G C D E F A B C D
WJEC	1 2 3	E F G C D E F A B C D
NISEG	Basic Intermediate Higher	E F G C D E F A B C D

THE NATIONAL CRITERIA

Certain topics have been selected by the Schools Examination Council as being so important that they must be included in the appropriate level examination if it is to be classified as a mathematics examination. These topics are displayed in two lists, forming a 'common core' to all syllabuses (See Table 2).

List 1 contains almost the whole of the syllabus content for all examinations in which the majority of candidates will be awarded grades E, F or G, i.e. for foundation or basic levels.

List 2 must, with List 1, be included in the syllabus of any examination in which a grade C can be awarded, and they must form almost all the syllabus content of an examination in which the majority of candidates are expected to be awarded grades C, D or E, i.e. for intermediate levels.

At the highest level, between 50% and 70% of the marks allocated to the written papers are to be given to questions on items in Lists 1 and 2.

From these conditions, we see that a thorough knowledge of the items in Lists 1 and 2 is essential for success in the examination.

Table 2: The National Criteria Lists

List 1	List 2
Whole numbers: odd, even, prime, square.	Natural numbers, integers, rational and irrational numbers.
Factors, multiples, idea of square root.	Square roots.
Directed numbers in practical situations.	Common factors, common multiples.
Vulgar and decimal fractions and percentages; equivalences between these forms in simple cases; conversion from vulgar to decimal fractions with the help of a calculator.	Conversion between vulgar and decimal fractions and percentages.
	Standard form.
Estimation.	
	Approximation to a given number of significant figures or decimal places.
Approximation to obtain reasonable answers.	Appropriate limits of accuracy.
The four rules applied to whole numbers and decimal fractions.	The four rules applied to vulgar (and mixed) fractions.
Language and notation of simple vulgar fractions in appropriate contexts, including addition and subtraction of vulgar (and mixed) fractions with simple denominators.	
Elementary ideas and notation of ratio.	Expression of one quantity as percentage of another.
Percentage of a sum of money.	Percentage change.
Scales, including map scales.	
Elementary ideas and applications of direct and inverse proportion.	Proportional division.
Common measures of rate.	
Efficient use of an electronic calculator; application of appropriate checks of accuracy.	
Measures of weight, length, area, volume and capacity in current units.	
Time: 24-hour and 12-hour clock.	
Money, including the use of foreign currencies.	
Personal and household finance, including hire purchase, interest, taxation, discount, loans, wages and salaries.	
Profit and loss; VAT.	
Reading of clocks and dials.	

List 1

Use of tables and charts.

Mathematical language used in the media.

Simple change of units including foreign currency.

Average speed.

Cartesian coordinates.

Interpretation and use of graphs in practical situations including travel graphs and conversion graphs.

Drawing graphs from given data.

The use of letters for generalized numbers.

Substitution of numbers for words and letters in formulae.

List 2

Constructing tables of values for given functions which include expressions of the form: $ax+b$, ax^2, $a/x(x \neq 0)$ where a and b are integral constants.

Drawing and interpretation of related graphs; idea of gradient.

Transformation of simple formulae.

Basic arithmetic processes expressed algebraically.

Directed numbers.

Use of brackets and extraction of common factors.

Positive and negative integral indices.

Simple linear equations in one unknown.

The geometrical terms: point, line, parallel, bearing, right angle, acute and obtuse angles, perpendicular, similarity.

Congruence.

Measurement of lines and angles.

Angles formed within parallel lines.

Angles at a point.

Enlargement.

Vocabulary of triangles, quadrilaterals and circles; properties of these figures directly related to their symmetries.

Properties of polygons directly related to their symmetries.

Angle in a semi-circle; angle between tangent and radius of a circle.

Angle properties of triangles and quadrilaterals.

Angle properties of regular polygons.

Simple solid figures.

Use of drawing instruments.

Practical applications based on simple locus properties.

List 1

Reading and making of scale drawings.

Perimeter and area of rectangle and triangle.

Circumference of circle.

Volume of cuboid.

Collection, classification and tabulation of statistical data.

Reading, interpreting and drawing simple inferences from tables and statistical diagrams.

Construction of bar charts and pictograms.

Measures of average and the purpose for which they are used.

Probability involving only one event.

List 2

Area of parallelogram.

Area of circle.

Volume of a cylinder.

Results of Pythagoras.

Sine, cosine and tangent for acute angles.

Application of these to calculation of a side or angle of a right-angled triangle.

Histogram with equal intervals.

Construction and use of pie-charts.

Construction and use of simple frequency distributions.

Simple combined probabilities.

Table 3: The syllabuses   F = Foundation; I = Intermediate; H = Higher

Examining group Syllabus Level	LEAG A			SMP			MEG			SMP		
	X	Y	Z	X	Y	Z	F	I	H	F	I	H
Numbers	✓	✓	✓	✓	✓	✓	✓	✓	✓	✓	✓	✓
Factors, multiples	✓	✓	✓	✓	✓	✓	✓	✓	✓	✓	✓	✓
Square roots	✓	✓	✓	✓	✓	✓	✓	✓	✓	✓	✓	✓
Directed numbers	✓	✓	✓	✓	✓	✓	✓	✓	✓	✓	✓	✓
Fractions and decimals	✓	✓	✓	✓	✓	✓	✓	✓	✓	✓	✓	✓
Percentages		✓	✓		✓	✓	✓	✓	✓	✓	✓	✓
Standard form		✓	✓		✓	✓		✓	✓	✓	✓	✓
Estimation	✓	✓	✓	✓	✓	✓	✓	✓	✓	✓	✓	✓
Approximation	✓	✓	✓	✓	✓	✓	✓	✓	✓	✓	✓	✓
Significant figures, decimal places		✓	✓			✓		✓	✓		✓	✓
Efficient use of electronic calculator	✓	✓	✓	✓	✓	✓	✓	✓	✓	✓	✓	✓
Profit and loss	✓	✓	✓	✓	✓	✓	✓	✓	✓	✓	✓	✓
Foreign currency	✓	✓	✓	✓	✓	✓	✓	✓	✓	✓	✓	✓
VAT and other practical problems	✓	✓	✓	✓	✓	✓	✓	✓	✓	✓	✓	✓
Simple interest	✓	✓	✓	✓	✓	✓	✓	✓	✓	✓	✓	✓
Compound interest								✓				
Ratio	✓	✓	✓	✓	✓	✓	✓	✓	✓	✓	✓	✓
Maps and scales	✓	✓	✓	✓	✓	✓	✓	✓	✓	✓	✓	✓
Direct and inverse proportion	✓	✓	✓	✓	✓	✓	✓	✓	✓	✓	✓	✓
Collection, classification of data	✓	✓	✓	✓	✓	✓	✓	✓	✓	✓	✓	✓
Bar charts and pictograms	✓	✓	✓	✓	✓	✓	✓	✓	✓	✓	✓	✓
Pie charts		✓	✓	✓	✓	✓	✓	✓	✓	✓	✓	✓
Frequency distributions		✓	✓	✓	✓	✓		✓	✓		✓	✓
Cumulative frequency diagrams (curves)								✓				✓
Calculation of mean		✓	✓	✓	✓	✓		✓	✓	✓	✓	✓
Location of mode and median		✓	✓	✓	✓	✓		✓	✓	✓	✓	✓
Probability, definition	✓	✓	✓	✓	✓	✓	✓	✓	✓	✓	✓	✓
Combined probabilities		✓	✓		✓	✓		✓	✓		✓	✓
Travel and conversion graphs	✓	✓	✓	✓	✓	✓	✓	✓	✓	✓	✓	✓
Graphs of given functions		✓	✓		✓	✓		✓	✓		✓	✓

NEA A			B(SMP)			SEG			WJEC			NISEC A			B(SMP)		
P	Q	R	P	Q	R	1	2	3	1	2	3	B	I	H	B	I	H
✓	✓	✓	✓	✓	✓	✓	✓	✓	✓	✓	✓	✓	✓	✓	✓	✓	✓
✓	✓	✓	✓	✓	✓	✓	✓	✓	✓	✓	✓	✓	✓	✓	✓	✓	✓
✓	✓	✓	✓	✓	✓	✓	✓	✓	✓	✓	✓	✓	✓	✓	✓	✓	✓
✓	✓	✓	✓	✓	✓	✓	✓	✓	✓	✓	✓	✓	✓	✓	✓	✓	✓
✓	✓	✓	✓	✓	✓	✓	✓	✓	✓	✓	✓	✓	✓	✓	✓	✓	✓
	✓	✓	✓	✓	✓		✓	✓		✓		✓			✓	✓	✓
✓	✓	✓	✓	✓	✓	✓	✓	✓	✓	✓	✓	✓	✓	✓	✓	✓	✓
	✓	✓		✓	✓		✓	✓		✓		✓	✓			✓	✓
✓	✓	✓	✓	✓	✓	✓	✓	✓	✓	✓	✓	✓	✓	✓	✓	✓	✓
✓	✓	✓	✓	✓	✓	✓	✓	✓	✓	✓	✓	✓	✓	✓	✓	✓	✓
	✓	✓	✓	✓	✓	✓	✓	✓	✓	✓	✓	✓	✓	✓	✓	✓	✓
													✓	✓		✓	✓
✓	✓	✓	✓	✓	✓	✓	✓	✓	✓	✓	✓	✓	✓	✓	✓	✓	✓
✓	✓	✓	✓	✓	✓	✓	✓	✓	✓	✓	✓	✓	✓	✓	✓	✓	✓
✓	✓	✓	✓	✓	✓	✓	✓	✓	✓	✓	✓	✓	✓	✓	✓	✓	✓
✓	✓	✓	✓	✓	✓	✓	✓	✓	✓	✓	✓	✓	✓	✓	✓	✓	✓
✓	✓	✓	✓	✓	✓	✓	✓	✓	✓	✓	✓	✓	✓	✓	✓	✓	✓
✓	✓	✓	✓	✓	✓	✓	✓	✓	✓	✓	✓	✓	✓	✓	✓	✓	✓
		✓			✓								✓	✓		✓	✓
✓	✓	✓	✓	✓	✓	✓	✓	✓	✓	✓	✓	✓	✓	✓	✓	✓	✓
																✓	✓
✓	✓	✓	✓	✓	✓	✓	✓	✓	✓	✓	✓	✓	✓	✓	✓	✓	✓
							✓	✓		✓	✓	✓	✓			✓	✓
✓	✓	✓	✓	✓	✓	✓	✓	✓	✓	✓	✓	✓	✓	✓	✓	✓	✓
✓	✓	✓		✓	✓	✓	✓	✓	✓	✓	✓	✓	✓	✓	✓	✓	✓

Examining group	LEAG			SMP			MEG			SMP		
Syllabus / Level	X	Y	Z	X	Y	Z	F	I	H	F	I	H
Graphical solution of simultaneous equations		✓	✓			✓		✓	✓		✓	✓
Gradient			✓		✓	✓		✓	✓		✓	✓
Trapezium rule for area under a graph			✓			✓		✓	✓			✓
Algebraic symbols	✓	✓	✓	✓	✓	✓	✓	✓	✓	✓	✓	✓
Factors		✓	✓		✓	✓		✓	✓		✓	✓
Positive and negative integer indices		✓	✓		✓	✓		✓	✓	✓	✓	✓
Simple linear equations		✓	✓		✓	✓		✓	✓	✓	✓	✓
Simultaneous linear equations			✓			✓		✓				
Quadratic equations			✓					✓				
Flow charts						✓					✓	✓
Iterative methods								✓				✓
Solutions of linear inequalities								✓				✓
Functional notation						✓		✓				✓
Composite functions						✓		✓				
Use of geometrical instruments	✓	✓	✓	✓	✓	✓	✓	✓	✓			✓
Angle properties of triangles and polygons	✓	✓	✓	✓	✓	✓	✓	✓	✓	✓	✓	✓
Parallel lines	✓	✓	✓	✓	✓	✓	✓	✓	✓	✓	✓	✓
Nets of solids	✓	✓	✓	✓	✓	✓	✓	✓	✓	✓	✓	✓
Similar and congruent figures		✓	✓		✓	✓		✓	✓	✓	✓	✓
Circle theorems		✓	✓		✓	✓		✓	✓		✓	✓
Tangent theorems			✓					✓				✓
Length of arc, area of sector												
Surface area of cylinder			✓			✓		✓				✓
Reflections, rotations, translations, enlargement	✓	✓	✓	✓	✓	✓	✓	✓	✓	✓	✓	✓
Matrices			✓			✓		✓				✓
Set language			✓				Used where applicable					
Venn diagrams			✓					✓				✓
Vectors			✓			✓		✓				✓
Trigonometry, sin, cos, tan, for acute angles		✓	✓		✓	✓		✓			✓	✓
Sine and cosine rules								✓				
Three dimensions, problems in			✓			✓		✓				✓

Q	R	B(SMP) P	Q	R	SEG 1	2	3	WJEC 1	2	3	NISEC A/B	I	H	B(SMP) B	I	H
✓	✓	✓	✓			✓	✓		✓	✓		✓	✓		✓	✓
✓	✓	✓	✓			✓	✓		✓	✓		✓	✓		✓	✓
		✓					✓									✓
✓	✓	✓	✓	✓	✓	✓	✓	✓	✓	✓		✓	✓		✓	✓
✓	✓		✓			✓	✓		✓	✓						
✓	✓		✓			✓	✓		✓	✓						
✓	✓	✓	✓			✓	✓		✓	✓	✓	✓	✓		✓	✓
	✓		✓				✓			✓		✓	✓			✓
	✓		✓				✓			✓		✓	✓			✓
			✓													
	✓		✓				✓					✓				✓
	✓		✓				✓					✓				✓
✓	✓		✓	✓		✓		✓								
	✓		✓													
✓	✓	✓	✓	✓	✓	✓	✓	✓	✓	✓	✓	✓	✓	✓	✓	✓
✓	✓	✓	✓	✓	✓	✓	✓	✓	✓	✓	✓	✓	✓	✓	✓	✓
✓	✓	✓	✓	✓	✓	✓	✓	✓	✓	✓	✓	✓	✓	✓	✓	✓
✓	✓	✓	✓	✓		✓	✓		✓	✓	✓	✓	✓		✓	✓
✓	✓	✓	✓			✓	✓			✓		✓	✓		✓	✓
	✓		✓				✓			✓		✓				✓
			✓													
			✓				✓			✓		✓				✓
			✓				✓			✓		✓				✓
✓	✓	✓	✓	✓	✓	✓	✓	✓	✓	✓	✓	✓	✓	✓	✓	✓
	✓		✓				✓					✓				✓
✓	✓		✓	✓			✓			✓						
	✓			✓			✓			✓						
✓	✓	✓	✓				✓			✓						
✓	✓	✓	✓	✓		✓	✓		✓	✓	✓		✓	✓	✓	✓
							✓			✓			✓		✓	✓
	✓			✓			✓			✓		✓				

GENERAL EXAMINATION HINTS

1   **Read the questions carefully**, especially all the *numbers* given. Wh is the scale given for the graph questions?

2   Try to **choose your questions carefully**; in particular, start with question you can do. It is most unlikely that you *must* start w question 1.

3   Always **make a rough estimate of any calculation**. If you are using calculator, set out each calculation clearly so that you (and t examiner) can see what you are trying to do.

4   **Draw a diagram** if the question is at all complicated. 'One picture worth a thousand words'.

5   Always **try to keep solutions as simple as possible** – if you fine difficult method, you may make a mistake in following it! I example, when solving isosceles triangles, draw the perpendicu bisector of the 'base'; do not use the sine or cosine formula.

6   **Do not cross out an answer** because you think that it is wrong. Part your solution may well be right, and you will lose the marks for thi you cross out the attempt.

7   If you have finished before the end of the examination, **check yc work carefully**.

8   If you are 'stuck' in one question, **check that you have used all t information given**, and see whether you can get any ideas from a earlier part of the question that you have already answered.

ARITHMETIC

CONTENTS

▶ **Summary** 25

▶ **Counting numbers** 25

▶ **Directed numbers** 26

▶ **Factors and multiples** 27
Squares and cubes   27

▶ **Time** 27

▶ **Number patterns** 28

▶ **Examination questions 1** 28

SUMMARY

- The **natural numbers** 1, 2, 3, 4 ... are those used for counting, and are called the **counting numbers**. The natural numbers are the counting numbers with the addition of zero, 0. The natural numbers are also called the **whole numbers** or the **cardinal numbers**.

- The **positive integers** are natural numbers greater than 0, i.e. 1, 2, 3, 4 ... The set of all positive integers is sometimes denoted by $\mathbf{Z}_+$, i.e. $\mathbf{Z}_+ = \{1, 2, 3, 4 ...\}$.

- The set of **all integers** is denoted by $\mathbf{Z}$, i.e. $\mathbf{Z} = \{... -4, -3, -2, -1, 0, 1, 2, 3, 4 ...\}$ **NB**: 0 is an integer but not a positive integer.

- **Rational numbers** are those obtained by dividing an integer by another integer, e.g. $\frac{3}{4}$. The set of all rational numbers is denoted by $\mathbf{Q}$, i.e. $\mathbf{Q} = \{... -\frac{3}{4}, ... -\frac{1}{8}, ... \frac{1}{4} ...\}$.

- All the numbers that we come across at this stage are **real** numbers, denoted by **R**. Numbers such as $\sqrt{-1}$ are not real numbers.

- Numbers that are not rational, but can be the roots of algebraic equations, e.g. $\sqrt{2}$, are called **irrational**. Those numbers, e.g. π, $\pi+1$, π^2, that cannot be the roots of such equations are called **transcendental** numbers.

- The numbers are represented by numerals (usually in **base** ten); the numerals may contain several digits, e.g. 345 has three digits. In base ten, 345 represents the number $3 \times 100 + 4 \times 10 + 5$.

- A number is **prime** if the number has no factors other than 1 and the number itself. It follows from this definition that 1 is **NOT** prime.

COUNTING NUMBERS

As we count sheep, we use a different number – one, two, three, four – at each stage to record how many sheep have passed, and if we write down these numbers we use **numerals** to denote them. We shall probably use the Arabic numerals 1, 2, 3, 4 ... and, if we use a different numeral for each number, we shall have to devise a system to prevent ourselves running out of symbols.

g. 1.1

Fig. 1.2

Babylonian

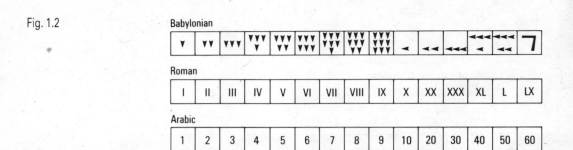

Roman

I	II	III	IV	V	VI	VII	VIII	IX	X	XX	XXX	XL	L	LX

Arabic

1	2	3	4	5	6	7	8	9	10	20	30	40	50	60

Fig. 1.3

For example, we can group the sheep in fives (as we do with tall marks – see Fig. 1.3) and record how many fives we have; we ca group in twelves (dozens) and gross ($12 \times 12 = 144$) using base 12; c use scores (20). However, since we almost invariably use number base 10, it is simplest if we group in tens, hundreds, thousands, etc.

Once the idea of a zero was added to the counting numbers, plac value enabled men to denote a number of any size using only the te symbols 0, 1, 2 . . . 9, the position of each digit giving additiona information, e.g. the number written 243 being:

$$2 \times 10^2 + \qquad 4 \times 10 \quad +3$$
two hundred and forty three

DIRECTED NUMBERS

Fig. 1.4

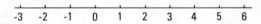

We can represent the numbers along a number line (Fig. 1.4), those t the right of zero being the positive numbers, those to the left bein the negative numbers. To denote a range of numbers, e.g. a numbers between 2 and 5, we shade that part of the number line:

Fig. 1.5

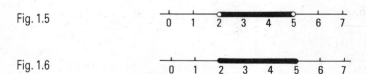

Fig. 1.6

If we do not wish to include the end numbers we use the notation i

Fig. 1.5; to denote all the numbers from 2 to 5 inclusive we shade the end circles, as in Fig. 1.6.

Directed numbers are commonly used in temperature changes and in bank balances. If the temperature is 4°C and it then falls by 6°C, the new temperature is −2°C. If we have £4 in the bank and draw out £6, we owe the bank £2 and our balance is −£2; this is called an overdraft and our account is overdrawn (written o/d usually).

FACTORS AND MULTIPLES

If a number x divides exactly into a number y, x is said to be a factor of y and y is said to be a multiple of x. Thus:

7 is a factor of 21
21 is a multiple of 7

SQUARES AND CUBES

A number that is the product of two equal numbers is called a perfect square, e.g. $16 = 4×4$, and so 16 is a perfect square. A number that is a product of three equal numbers is called a perfect cube, e.g. $27 = 3×3×3$, and so 27 is a perfect cube.

TIME

Almost all the systems of units used are now decimal. Among the few exceptions are the units of time, the smallest unit in common use being of course the second.

60 seconds = 1 minute
60 minutes = 1 hour
24 hours = 1 day

Take care to remember this when reading questions involving time.

Specimen question An aircraft leaves London at 23.30 and lands at Lagos after a flight of 6 hours 40 minutes. At what time does it land in Lagos?

Answer

23.30
6.40+
‾‾‾‾‾
30.10 (using 60 minutes = 1 hour)
= 6.10 next day

Notice that 23.30 is 30 minutes before the end of the 24-hour day; 30 minutes taken from the 6.40 flight time of 6 hours 40 minutes leaves 6 hours 10 minutes, so that the arrival time is 6.10 next day. Sometim the notation 06.10 h will be seen.

NUMBER PATTERNS

It is often useful and interesting to spot any kind of pattern, and son of the easiest to spot are number patterns and geometric patterns (s pages 29 and 30). Spotting number patterns usually requires that v are already familiar with many simple patterns; for example:

7, 26, 63, 124

are each one less than consecutive cubes:

8, 27, 64, 125

If the pattern cannot be spotted immediately, the method in th following example of repeated subtraction often helps find later tern in any sequence.

Specimen question Find a possible fifth term in the sequence 7, 26, 6 124.

Answer Find the differences between successive terms and set out th values as in Fig. 1.7.

Fig. 1.7

```
7    26    63    124
   19    37    61
      18    24
          6
```

Fig. 1.8

```
7    26    63    124   215
   19    37    61    91↗
      18    24    30↗
          6 → 6↗
```

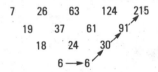

Add another term 6 to the bottom line and work upwards (Fig. 1.8).

We must remember that there may be several sequences that w produce any given set of numbers. The numbers 7, 26, 63, could com from a sequence that has 118 as the fourth term. Calculate the di ferences and see why.

EXAMINATION QUESTIONS 1

1 Identify which of the following are:

(*a*) primes;

(*b*) perfect squares;

   (c)   factors of 120;

   (d)   multiples of 6.

        1, 3, 7, 9, 15, 16, 18, 24, 43, 48

2   Write each of the following as a product of prime factors, and so find the square root of each number:

   (a)   196;

   (b)   324;

   (c)   1764.

3   Express as a product of prime factors:

   (a)   144;

   (b)   216;

   (c)   441;

   (d)   512.

State which of these numbers are perfect squares and which perfect cubes.

4   (a)   Write down any rational number between $\frac{3}{4}$ and $\frac{4}{5}$.

   (b)   Write down any rational number between 1.4 and 1.5.

   (c)   Write down any rational number between $\sqrt{2}$ and $\sqrt{3}$.

5   Write down any irrational number between 3 and 4.

6   A film started at 20.15 h. Tom arrived 20 minutes before the film started. At what time did he arrive? The film lasted 2 hours 50 minutes. At what time did it finish?

7   Jock's flight from Aberdeen arrived at Birmingham at 00.30 h. It had taken 1 hr 50 minutes. At what time had it left Aberdeen?

8   The temperature in Paris one day was 4°C. Moscow was 12°C colder than Paris. What was the temperature in Moscow that day?

9   Mary was £15.60 overdrawn at the bank. When she paid in £44 cash, how much had she to her credit?

10   Suggest suitable numbers for the next term in each sequence, giving reasons to justify your suggestions:

   (a)   1, 2, 3, 4

   (b)   1, 2, 3, 5

   (c)   1, 2, 3, 6

   (d)   1, 2, 4, 7

   (e)   2, 5, 10, 17

   (f)   2, 5, 10, 18

11   Simplify:

$$\frac{1+3}{2+4}, \quad \frac{1+3+5}{2+4+6}, \quad \frac{1+3+5+7}{2+4+6+8},$$

and suggest a likely value for:

$$\frac{1+3+5+7 \ldots 199}{2+4+6+ \ \ldots 200}$$

12   Using rectangular tiles 2 ft by 1 ft, a strip of wall 2 ft high and 1 ft long can be tiled in only one way (Fig. 1.9(a)); a strip 2 ft high and 2 ft long can be tiled in two ways (Fig. 1.9(b)); a strip 2 ft high and 3 ft long in

three ways (Fig. 1.9(c)). By drawing suitable diagrams find in how many ways it is possible, with these tiles, to tile a strip of wall 2 ft high and 4 ft long, and a strip 2 ft high and 5 ft long.

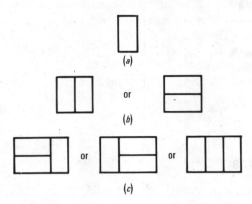

Find a relation between the five numbers in the series beginning:

1, 2, 3 . . .

to suggest in how many ways it is possible to tile a strip of wall 2 ft high and 6 ft long.

If x_n is the number of ways in which it is possible to tile a strip of wall 2 ft high and n ft long, use Fig. 1.10 to find a relation between x_{n-2}, x_{n-1} and x_n.

Fig. 1.10

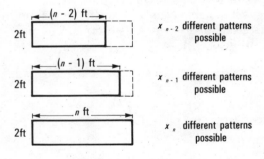

FRACTIONS AND DECIMALS; PERCENTAGES

CONTENTS

▶ **Summary** 33

▶ **Fractions** 33
Addition and subtraction of fractions   33
Multiplication of fractions   34
Division of fractions   34

▶ **Decimals** 35

▶ **Percentages** 36

▶ **Examination questions 2** 37

SUMMARY

♦ **Rational numbers** are those obtained by dividing one integer by another integer, e.g. $\frac{7}{4}, \frac{14}{12}$. These are called **vulgar** (i.e. common) **fractions**.

♦ In a fraction, e.g. $\frac{3}{4}$, the number on the top line (here 3) is called the **numerator** and the number on the bottom (here 4) the **denominator**. If the numerator and denominator have a common factor, we can divide by that factor, e.g. $\frac{6}{8} = \frac{3}{4}$.

♦ In a **proper fraction**, the numerator is less than the denominator, e.g. $\frac{3}{4}$ is a proper fraction, but $\frac{5}{4}$ is an **improper** fraction.

♦ A **decimal** (or decimal fraction) is a fraction whose denominator is a power of ten, e.g. $0.7 = \frac{7}{10}, 0.21 = \frac{21}{100}$.

♦ **Percentages** are fractions with a denominator of 100, e.g. $77\% = \frac{77}{100}$.

♦ The **highest common factor** (hcf) of two numbers is the largest number that is a factor of each, e.g. the hcf of 75 and 120 is 15.

♦ The **lowest common multiple** (lcm) of two numbers is the smallest number of which both are factors, e.g. the lcm of 75 and 120 is 600.

FRACTIONS

To share a bar of chocolate fairly with a friend, we divide it into two halves. To share with two friends we divide it into thirds; to share with three friends into quarters. The idea of these easy fractions is familiar to us all. To manipulate them, though, we need a few simple rules.

ADDITION AND SUBTRACTION OF FRACTIONS

In a fraction, say $\frac{3}{4}$, we call the term on the top line, here 3, the **numerator**, and the term on the bottom line, here 4, **denominator**. The denominator tells us into how many parts the whole has been divided; the numerator tells us how many of those parts we are now considering.

To add $\frac{1}{5}$ to $\frac{2}{5}$, we notice that the denominators are the same, so that both fractions refer to the same sized parts of a whole, here fifths. We can therefore add the parts, $\frac{1}{5} + \frac{2}{5} = \frac{3}{5}$.

If the denominators are not the same, then we must express each fraction in a form with equal denominators, which will be the lcm (see summary) of the denominators. Thus $\frac{1}{5} + \frac{7}{10} = \frac{2}{10} + \frac{7}{10} = \frac{9}{10}$, and $\frac{2}{3} - \frac{1}{2} = \frac{4}{6} - \frac{3}{6} = \frac{1}{6}$.

Specimen question Find the value of

(a) $\frac{1}{3}+\frac{1}{4}+\frac{1}{6}$,

(b) $2\frac{2}{3}-1\frac{5}{6}$,

Answer

(a)   The lcm of 3, 4 and 6 is 12, so we write each fraction with a denominator 12. Thus:

$$\tfrac{1}{3}+\tfrac{1}{4}+\tfrac{1}{6} = \tfrac{4}{12}+\tfrac{3}{12}+\tfrac{2}{12} = \tfrac{9}{12} = \tfrac{3}{4}$$

(b)   We can consider the whole numbers separately, and subtract 1 from 2 to give 1. When we come to the fractions, though, we see that $\frac{2}{3}-\frac{5}{6} = \frac{4}{6}-\frac{5}{6} = -\frac{1}{6}$. Thus we have:

$$2\tfrac{2}{3}-1\tfrac{5}{6} = 1+(\tfrac{2}{3}-\tfrac{5}{6}) = 1-\tfrac{1}{6} = \tfrac{5}{6} \ (\text{using } 1 = \tfrac{6}{6})$$

MULTIPLICATION OF FRACTIONS

If a bar of chocolate has been divided into thirds, and each piece is then halved, we have six equal pieces, each one-sixth of the whole. Thus $\frac{1}{2}$ of $\frac{1}{3}$ is $\frac{1}{6}$. More generally, we have:

$$\frac{a}{b}\times\frac{c}{d}=\frac{ac}{bd}$$

This result only applies to fractions, not to mixed numbers like $3\frac{1}{2}$. Thus:

$$\tfrac{2}{5}\times\tfrac{3}{4} = \tfrac{6}{20} = \tfrac{3}{10}$$

and

$$\tfrac{5}{6}\times\tfrac{2}{5} = \tfrac{10}{30} = \tfrac{1}{3}$$

DIVISION OF FRACTIONS

The value of a fraction is unaltered if the numerator and denominator are multiplied by the same number, so that:

$$\frac{\frac{2}{3}}{\frac{3}{4}} = \frac{\frac{2}{3}\times 4}{3} = \frac{\frac{8}{3}}{3} = \tfrac{8}{9}$$

This can be summarized by saying that the fraction which is the divisor should be inverted, and then multiplication carried out. But it is much clearer if we ignore that rule, and think merely of multiplying numerator and denominator at each stage, as above, instead of:

$$\frac{\frac{2}{3}}{\frac{3}{4}} = \tfrac{2}{3}\times\tfrac{4}{3} = \tfrac{8}{9}$$

Specimen question Simplify $\dfrac{\frac{2}{5}}{\frac{3}{8}}$.

Answer:

$$\frac{\frac{2}{5}}{\frac{3}{8}} = \frac{\frac{2}{5} \times 8}{3} = \frac{16}{3 \times 5} = \frac{16}{15}$$

DECIMALS

In the same way that we use the place of a digit to indicate the power of ten by which it is multiplied, we can, having introduced a decimal marker (usually a point . though a comma , is used in some countries) place the digits to the right of that marker to indicate the power of ten by which the number is divided. Thus:

$$0.2 = \frac{2}{10}, \, 0.13 = \frac{13}{10^2} = \frac{13}{100}$$

and:

$$0.004 = \frac{4}{10^3} = \frac{4}{1000}$$

These decimals are manipulated in the same way as numbers without a decimal marker, though care must be taken to see that the decimal marker is positioned correctly.

Specimen question Find the value of
(a) $(0.2)^2$,
(b) $(0.4)^2$,
(c) $(0.2)^3$,
(d) $\dfrac{0.6}{0.2}$,
(e) $\dfrac{0.04}{0.2}$

Answer
(a) $(0.2)^2 = 0.2 \times 0.2 = \frac{2}{10} \times \frac{2}{10} = \frac{4}{100} = 0.04$
(b) $(0.4)^2 = 0.4 \times 0.4 = \frac{4}{10} \times \frac{4}{10} = \frac{16}{100} = 0.16$
(c) $(0.2)^3 = 0.2 \times 0.2 \times 0.2 = \frac{2}{10} \times \frac{2}{10} \times \frac{2}{10} = \frac{8}{1000} = 0.008$
(d)   Since a fraction is unaltered if the numerator and denominator are multiplied by the same number:

$$\frac{0.6}{0.2} = \frac{6}{2} = 3$$

(e) $\dfrac{0.04}{0.2} = \dfrac{4}{20} = \dfrac{2}{10} = 0.2$

When decimals are multiplied together, the number of digits to the right of the decimal marker in the product is equal to the sum of the number of digits to the right of the marker in the numbers being multiplied together. Care should be taken of any final zeros in the product, for example:

$$0.2 \times 0.03 = 0.006 \quad (1+2=3)$$
$$0.02 \times 0.004 = 0.000\,08 \quad (2+3=5)$$

but:

$$0.02 \times 0.005 = 0.000\,10 \quad (2+3=5)$$

(In the last example, a fifth digit only occurs in the product if we retain the zero on the far right, obtained from $2 \times 5 = 10$.)

A similar rule can be devised for division, though it is almost invariably easier to avoid division by a decimal by multiplying numerator and denominator by a suitably large power of ten, e.g.:

$$\frac{0.005}{0.02} = \frac{0.5}{2} = 0.25$$

and:

$$\frac{0.108}{0.0004} = \frac{1080}{4} = 270$$

Specimen question Simplify:

$$\frac{(0.5)^2 + 2}{0.09}$$

Answer Work out the bracket first: $(0.5)^2 = 0.25$. So:

$$\frac{(0.5)^2 + 2}{0.09} = \frac{2.25}{0.09}$$

Multiply numerator and denominator of the fraction by 100:

$$\frac{(0.5)^2 + 2}{0.09} = \frac{2.25}{0.09} = \frac{225}{9} = 25$$

PERCENTAGES

Suppose that in a certain box of 50 eggs, 7 are bad. Then we can say that the ratio of the number of bad eggs to the total number of eggs is 7:50, which is equal to 14:100. A ratio in which the second term is 100 can be put as a percentage, here 14 per cent (or 14%). We see that:

- 14% is equivalent to the ratio 14:100 or 7:50;
- 14% is equivalent to the fraction $\frac{14}{100}$;
- 14% is equivalent to the decimal 0.14.

Some of the simpler percentages can easily be expressed as fractions:
- 75% is $\frac{3}{4}$

- $66\frac{2}{3}\%$ is $\frac{2}{3}$
- 50% is $\frac{1}{2}$
- $33\frac{1}{3}\%$ is $\frac{1}{3}$
- 25% is $\frac{1}{4}$

To express one quantity as a percentage of another, first write it as a fraction of the second quantity, then multiply by 100.

Specimen question One Saturday Everton scored 7 of the 35 goals scored in the First Division. What percentage was this of the goals scored?

Answer The percentage of the goals scored by Everton was:

$\frac{7}{35} \times 100$, i.e. 20%

Specimen question Write 55% as a fraction in its lowest terms.

Answer

$$55\% = \frac{55}{100} = \frac{11}{20}$$

EXAMINATION QUESTIONS 2

1 Find what fraction each shaded region in Fig. 2.1 is of the whole, expressing your answers as fractions in their lowest terms.

Fig. 2.1

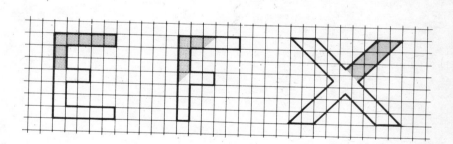

2 Find the value of:
 (a) $\frac{1}{3}+\frac{1}{4}$
 (b) $\frac{2}{3}+\frac{3}{4}-\frac{1}{6}$
 (c) $\frac{5}{3}\times\frac{1}{2}-\frac{1}{12}$
 (d) $\frac{5}{3}\times\frac{1}{4}+\frac{3}{4}\times\frac{1}{6}$

3 Find the value of:
 (a) $1\frac{1}{3}+2\frac{1}{2}$
 (b) $2\frac{1}{3}-3\frac{1}{2}+1\frac{1}{4}$
 (c) $\frac{1}{2}(3\frac{1}{3}-2\frac{1}{2})$
 (d) $\frac{1}{2}\times1\frac{1}{2}\times3\frac{1}{3}-2\frac{1}{2}$

4 Express each of the following fractions as its decimal equivalent:
 (a) $\frac{1}{8}$

(b) $\frac{1}{25}$

(c) $\frac{7}{50}$

(d) $\frac{71}{500}$

5   Express each of the following decimals as a fraction in its lowest terms:

(a)   0.25

(b)   0.24

(c)   0.375

6   Express each of the following as a percentage:

(a) $\frac{1}{5}$

(b) $\frac{3}{20}$

(c) $\frac{37}{250}$

7   Express each of the following as a decimal equivalent:

(a)   17%

(b) $17\frac{1}{2}$%

(c) $117\frac{1}{2}$%

8   Express each of the following as a fraction in its lowest terms:

(a)   15%

(b) $27\frac{1}{2}$%

(c) $37\frac{1}{2}$%

9   One Saturday, four-fifths of the pupils in a school went to watch the school football team in a match. One-quarter of them travelled by bus. If there were 164 pupils travelling by bus, how many pupils were there in the school?

10 Whiteside toothpaste is sold in three sizes (see Fig. 2.2).

Fig. 2.2

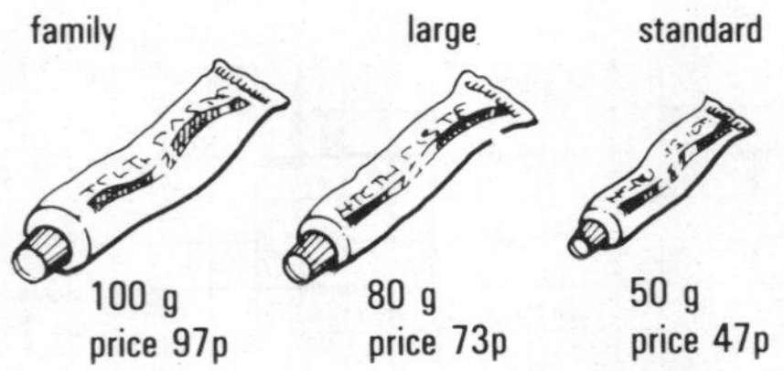

family   large   standard

100 g   80 g   50 g
price 97p   price 73p   price 47p

Which size is the best value for money? Describe how you reached your answer.   [*SEG specimen question*]

INDICES; NUMBERS IN STANDARD FORM

CONTENTS

▶ **Summary**

41

▶ **Indices**

41

▶ **Examination questions 3A**
Negative and functional indices   43

42

▶ **Examination questions 3B**

44

▶ **Standard form**
Manipulating numbers in standard form   44

44

▶ **Examination questions 3C**

45

SUMMARY

- The **laws of indices** are as follows.

$$a^m \times a^n = a^{m+n}$$

$$a^m \div a^n = a^{m-n}$$

$$(a^m)^n = a^{mn}, \text{ e.g. } (2^3)^4 = 2^{12}$$

$$a^{-m} = \frac{1}{a^m}, \text{ in particular } a^{-1} = \frac{1}{a}$$

$$a^0 = 1$$

$$a^{1/p} = {}^p\sqrt{a}, \text{ in particular } a^{\frac{1}{2}} = \sqrt{a}$$

$$a^{q/p} = ({}^p\sqrt{a})^q$$

- Numbers written $A \times 10^n$ are in **standard form**, where:

$$1 \leq A < 10$$

and n is an integer, e.g.:

$$2700 = 2.7 \times 10^3 \text{ and } 0.027 = 2.7 \times 10^{-2}$$

INDICES

We write $2 \times 2 \times 2 \times 2$ as 2^4, so that:

$$(2 \times 2 \times 2 \times 2) \times (2 \times 2 \times 2) = 2^4 \times 2^3$$

and:

$$2 \times 2 \times 2 \times 2 \times 2 \times 2 \times 2 = 2^7$$

i.e.:

$$2^4 \times 2^3 = 2^7$$

Notice that we add the indices when we multiply the two numbers. Similarly:

$$\frac{2^5}{2^3} = \frac{2 \times 2 \times 2 \times 2 \times 2}{2 \times 2 \times 2} = 2 \times 2 = 2^2$$

so that when we divide we subtract the indices.

We notice that:

$$(2\times2\times2)^2 = (2^3)^2 = 2^6$$

so that in general:

$$(a^3)^2 = a^6$$

and also:

$$\sqrt{a^6} = a^3$$

Specimen question Express as powers of prime numbers:
(a)   32;
(b)   3200.

Answer
(a) $32 = 2\times2\times2\times2\times2 = 2^5$
(b) $3200 = 32\times100 = 2^5\times100 = 2^5\times2^2\times5^2$
                                            $= 2^7\times5^2$

Specimen question Given that x and y are integers, find x and y if:

$$2^x3^y = 144$$

Answer Express 144 in terms of its prime factors:

$$144 = 2\times2\times2\times2\times3\times3 = 2^4\times3^2$$

If:

$$2^x\times3^y = 2^4\times3^2$$

and x and y are integers, then $x=4$ and $y=3$.

EXAMINATION QUESTIONS 3A

1   If $x = 2^3\times3$ and $y = 2\times3^2$, express in powers of 2 and 3:
      (a) xy
      (b) x^2
      (c) $12xy$
      (d) $6x^2y$
      (e) $(xy)^2$
      (f) $(x^2)^6$
      (g) xy^2
      (h) $\dfrac{x^2}{y}$
      (i) $\dfrac{x^3}{2y}$
      (j) $\dfrac{x^4}{12y}$

2   Express as powers of 2 and 3:
  (a)   12
  (b)   48
  (c)   162
  (d)   486

3   If x and y are integers, find x and y, given that:
  (a) $72 = 2^x 3^y$
  (b) $45 = x \times 3^y$

NEGATIVE AND FRACTIONAL INDICES

Since:

$$\frac{a^5}{a^2} = a^3$$

and $5 - 2 = 3$, we can write $\dfrac{1}{a^2}$ as a^{-2}, and:

$$\frac{a^5}{a^2} = a^5 \times \frac{1}{a^2} = a^5 \times a^{-2} = a^3$$

as expected. Thus:

$$a^{-n} \text{ means } \frac{1}{a^n}$$

and in particular:

$$a^{-1} = \frac{1}{a}$$

Since we add the indices when multiplying powers of a number a, to find a meaning for $a^{\frac{1}{2}}$, we see:

$$a^{\frac{1}{2}} \times a^{\frac{1}{2}} = a^1 = a$$

so that $a^{\frac{1}{2}}$ is the square root of a. Similarly:

$$a^{\frac{1}{3}} \times a^{\frac{1}{3}} \times a^{\frac{1}{3}} = a^1 = a$$

so that $a^{\frac{1}{3}}$ is the cube root of a. In general:

$$a^{1/n} = \sqrt[n]{a}, \text{ the } n\text{th root of } a$$

We can give a value to a^0, for:

$$a^m \times a^0 = a^{m+0} = a^m$$

so that:

$$a^0 = \frac{a^m}{a^m} = 1$$

Examples
  (a) $2^{-1} = \frac{1}{2}$
  (b) $4^{\frac{1}{2}} = \sqrt{4} = 2$

(c) $\qquad 9^{-\frac{1}{2}} = \dfrac{1}{9^{\frac{1}{2}}} = \dfrac{1}{\sqrt{9}} = \dfrac{1}{3}$

(d) $\qquad 4^{\frac{3}{2}} = 4^{\frac{1}{2}} \times 4^{\frac{1}{2}} \times 4^{\frac{1}{2}} = 2 \times 2 \times 2 = 2^3 = 8$

(e) $\qquad 2^0 = 1$

EXAMINATION QUESTIONS 3B

Write down the value of the following.

1   3^{-2}
2    $8^{\frac{1}{3}}$
3    $36^{\frac{1}{2}}$
4    $16^{\frac{1}{4}}$
5   4^{-1}
6    $100^{\frac{1}{2}}$
7   5^0
8    $25^{-\frac{1}{2}}$
9   7^0
10   $25^{\frac{3}{2}}$

STANDARD FORM

An average adult has about 20 000 000 000 000 red corpuscles in his system; the diameter of a bacterium is 0.000 02 cm. Numbers like these are difficult to write and hard to manipulate, and we usually write them in standard form (sometimes called standard index form), 2×10^{13} and 2×10^{-5}, i.e. in the form $A \times 10^n$, where A is a number between 1 and 10 (including 1 but not 10) and n is an integer, positive or negative. Thus we write:

$$2700 = 2.7 \times 10^3 \qquad\qquad 0.27 \;\;= 2.7 \times 10^{-1}$$
$$270 = 2.7 \times 10^2 \text{ and } 0.027 \;= 2.7 \times 10^{-2}$$
$$27 = 2.7 \times 10 \qquad\quad 0.0027 = 2.7 \times 10^{-3}$$

To express a number in standard form, put a decimal marker after the first non-zero digit, then find the correct power of ten, thus:

$$27\,000 = 2.7 \times 10\,000 \;= 2.7 \times 10^4$$
$$0.000\,27 = 2.7 \times 0.000\,1 = 2.7 \times 10^{-4}$$

MANIPULATING NUMBERS IN STANDARD FORM

The powers of ten have to be treated as indices, so that they are added when the numbers are multiplied, and subtracted when the numbers are divided. Thus:

$$(3 \times 10^4) \times (2 \times 10^5) = 6 \times 10^9$$
$$(3 \times 10^4) \times (4 \times 10^5) = 12 \times 10^9 = 1.2 \times 10^{10}$$
$$(3 \times 10^4) \div (2 \times 10^5) = 1.5 \times 10^{-1}$$
$$(3 \times 10^4) \div (4 \times 10^5) = 0.75 \times 10^{-1} = 7.5 \times 10^{-2}$$

Notice that in two of the above examples we did not at first have standard form. We had to write $12 = 1.2 \times 10$ and $0.75 = 7.5 \times 10^{-1}$.
NB Take care with negative indices.

Examples Carry out the following calculations, leaving each answer in standard form.

(a) $(4 \times 10^2) \times (7 \times 10^3)$ $= 28 \times 10^5$ $= 2.8 \times 10^6$
(b) $(4 \times 10^2) \times (7 \times 10^{-4})$ $= 28 \times 10^{-2} = 2.8 \times 10^{-1}$
(c) $(4 \times 10^{-2}) \times (7 \times 10^{-4}) = 28 \times 10^{-6} = 2.8 \times 10^{-5}$
(d) $(7 \times 10^5) \div (4 \times 10^2)$ $= 1.75 \times 10^3$
(e) $(3 \times 10^5) \div (4 \times 10^2)$ $= 0.75 \times 10^3 = 7.5 \times 10^2$
(f) $(3 \times 10^5) \div (4 \times 10^{-2})$ $= 0.75 \times 10^7 = 7.5 \times 10^6$

EXAMINATION QUESTIONS 3C

1 Write each of the following numbers in ordinary form.
  (a) 3×10^2
  (b) 3.7×10^3
  (c) 3.07×10^4
  (d) 3×10^{-1}
  (e) 3×10^{-3}

2 Write each of the following numbers in standard form.
  (a)   780
  (b)   678 000
  (c)   0.008
  (d)   0.1

3 Find the value, in standard form, of:
  (a) $(3 \times 10^2) \times (2 \times 10^3)$
  (b) $(3 \times 10^2) \div (2 \times 10^3)$
  (c) $(3 \times 10^2) \div (2 \times 10^{-3})$
  (d) $(3 \times 10^{-2}) \div (2 \times 10^{-3})$

4 Find the value of x/y when:
  (a) $x = 4 \times 10^3$, $y = 2 \times 10^5$
  (b) $x = 3 \times 10^4$, $y = 4 \times 10^7$

EFFICIENT USE OF THE CALCULATOR

CONTENTS

▶ **Summary** 49

▶ **Efficient use of the calculator** 49
Use of brackets   50
Evaluating polynomials   50

▶ **Examination questions 4A** 50

▶ **Degree of accuracy** 51
Significant figures   51
Decimal places   52

▶ **Estimates of calculations** 52

▶ **Examination questions 4B** 53

SUMMARY

♦ The buttons most likely to be needed on a calculator, either as:

first functions   ☐

or

second functions   ☐ ☐
(inv)

are:

inv		1/x		$\sqrt{}$	x^2		x^y
+/–				sin	cos	tan	
$a^{b/c}$	[ ]						
7	8	9		C	AC		
4	5	6		×	÷		
1	2	3		+	–		
0	.			=			

♦ Significant figures – start counting at the first non-zero digit, e.g. 0.020 34 = 0.0203 to 3sf.
♦ Decimal places – start counting at the decimal point, e.g. 0.020 34 = 0.020 to 3dp.

EFFICIENT USE OF THE CALCULATOR

Calculators vary, and the manner in which they operate varies a little. Check that you understand the sequence in which operations are carried out on your calculator. For example, check these:

$$12 \times 3 + 4 = 40$$
$$12 - 3 \times 4 = 0$$
$$12 - 3 \div 4 = 11.25$$
$$\tfrac{1}{2} + 3 = 3.5$$

In particular, check the three following calculations:

1 $\dfrac{1}{2+3} = 0.2$

2 $\dfrac{1}{2+3\times6} = 0.05$

3 $\dfrac{1}{2+3\div6} = 0.4$

Depending on the type of calculator that you have, you may need to use brackets to obtain the correct order of operations in **1**, **2** and **3**.

USE OF BRACKETS

The convention that we use in arithmetic is that multiplication and division are carried out before addition and subtraction, but the ambiguity arises in **1**, **2** and **3** because the division line of the fraction is really a division sign. If we did not use brackets, we may have obtained 3.5 when evaluating **1**, i.e. $1 \div 2 + 3$. We may have to key into the calculator $1 \div (2+3)$ in order to evaluate:

$$\frac{1}{2+3}$$

EVALUATING POLYNOMIALS

When drawing the graph of a function like:

$$y = x^3 - 4x^2 - 5x$$

we may make out a table of values like Table 4.1.

Table 4.1

x	-3	-2	-1
x^3	-27	-8	-1
$-4x^2$	-36	-16	-4
$-5x$	15	10	5
$y = x^3 - 4x^2 - 5x$	-48	-14	0

When we have a calculator it is quicker to use brackets and to re-arrange:

$$x^3 - 4x^2 - 5x \quad \text{as} \quad x[x(x-4)-5].$$

To find the value of y when $x = -3$:

$$y = -3(-3(-3-4)-5)$$
$$= -3(21-5)$$
$$= -48$$

the value of y when $x = -2$ is:

$$y = -2(-2(-2-4)-5)$$
$$= -2(12-5)$$
$$= -14$$

etc.

EXAMINATION QUESTIONS 4A

Give all answers to an appropriate degree of accuracy.

1   Given that $A = 2\pi r(r+h)$ find the value of A when:
   (a) $r = 4, h = 6$, taking π to be 3;
   (b) $r = 4.12, h = 5.75$, taking π from your calculator.

2   Given that:

$$\frac{1}{f} = \frac{1}{u} + \frac{1}{v}$$

find f when:

(a) $u = 2$, $v = 4$;
(b) $u = 2.49$, $v = 3.87$.

3   Given that:

$$s = \frac{v^2 - u^2}{2a}$$

find s when:
(a) $v = 5$, $u = 3$, $a = 4$;
(b) $v = 4.974$, $u = 3.123$, $a = 3.775$.

4   Writing $f(x) = x^3 - 4x^2 - 6x$
in the form $f(x) = x(x(x-4)-6)$

find the value of:

(a) $f(7)$
(b) $f(7.093)$
(c) $f(19.783)$

5   If

$$f(x) = x^4 - 4.01x^3 - 8.52x^2 + 7.39x + 15.32$$

evaluate:

(a) $f(1)$
(b) $f(1.08)$
(c) $f(7.84)$

6   British Telecom send out domestic telephone accounts quarterly. For the first quarter of 1985, the charge was made up of a rental of £19.15 plus 4.7p for each dialled unit. Value Added Tax at 15% was then added to the total. In this quarter Mr and Mrs Thomson used 882 dialled units. Calculate, correct to the nearest penny, the amount of their quarterly account.   [*MEG specimen question*]

DEGREE OF ACCURACY

SIGNIFICANT FIGURES   The distance between two posts on an airfield may be measured as 2123 m 45 cm, i.e. 2123.45 m. Even this is most unlikely to be exact, and better instruments might give 2123.456, or even more decimal places. For many purposes, 2100 m will be sufficiently accurate, and this degree of accuracy is called 'correct to two significant figures'.

For 'significant figures', start counting at the first non-zero digit; the usual convention (there are other conventions, such as correcting to the nearest even number, or the nearest odd number – ignore them at present) is that if the digit next after the required number is 5 or more, then the number is 'rounded up', e.g.

$$43\,496 = 40\,000 \text{ to 1 significant figure}$$
$$= 43\,000 \text{ to 2 significant figures}$$
$$= 43\,500 \text{ to 3 significant figures}$$
$$= 43\,500 \text{ to 4 significant figures}$$

the first zero counting as a significant digit, as it follows the non-zero 5. The position of the decimal point does not affect the significant figures, e.g.

$$0.045\,036 = 0.05 \quad \text{to 1 significant figure}$$
$$= 0.045 \text{ to 2 significant figures}$$
$$= 0.0450 \text{ to 3 significant figures}$$

zeros only counting when they follow non-zero digits.

DECIMAL PLACES

In some calculations we require results 'correct to a certain number of decimal places', which means that we start counting at the decimal point, however many digits are to the left of that decimal point. Thus:

$$435.678 \quad = 435.68 \text{ to 2 decimal places}$$
$$4.356\,78 = \quad 4.36 \text{ to 2 decimal places}$$
$$0.043\,56 = \quad 0.04 \text{ to 2 decimal places.}$$

ESTIMATES OF CALCULATIONS

It is most important that we always carry out a rough check of our calculations, and to do this we shall want to make a suitable approximation to the numbers in a calculation. Often 1 significant figure is appropriate.

Specimen question Correct each number to 1 significant figure, and so estimate the value of:

$$\frac{0.43 \times 5.7}{0.078}$$

Answer Correcting each number to 1 significant figure:

$$\frac{0.43 \times 5.7}{0.078} = \frac{0.4 \times 6}{0.08}$$

$$= \frac{240}{8}$$

$$= 30$$

1 Correct each of the following to 2 significant figures:
   5321; 5371; 5351; 0.5321; 0.5032; 0.5003.

2 Correct each of the following to 2 decimal places:
   5.352; 5.357; 5.355; 5.350; 0.5503; 0.5553; 0.5053; 0.5005.

3 Correct each number to 1 significant figure, and so estimate the value of:

   (a) $\pi \times (4.3)^2$

   (b) $\pi \times 4.3 \times 5.7$

   (c) $\dfrac{\pi}{\sqrt{124}}$

   (d) $\dfrac{(9.87)^2}{6.4 + (2.1)^2}$

RATIO AND PERCENTAGE; TAXES

CONTENTS

▶ **Summary** 57

▶ **Ratio** 57

▶ **Examination questions 5A** 58

▶ **Percentages** 58

▶ **Examination questions 5B** 59
Percentage change   59

▶ **Taxes** 60

▶ **Examination questions 5C** 61

▶ **Percentage profit and loss** 61

▶ **Examination questions 5D** 63

SUMMARY

- If x is twice y, we say that the ratio of x to y is 2 to 1, i.e. $x:y = 2:1$.
- Percentage is merely a fraction with a denominator of 100, e.g.

$$17\% = \frac{17}{100}$$

- If a quantity a is increased by $x\%$, the new value is:

$$\frac{100+x}{100} \times a$$

- If a quantity has been increased by $x\%$ and its new value is b, the old value was:

$$\frac{100}{100+x} \times b$$

- Percentage error $= \dfrac{\text{Error}}{\text{Correct measurement}} \times 100$

- Percentage profit $= \dfrac{\text{Profit}}{\text{Price for which it was bought by the seller}} \times 100$

RATIO

A map may be drawn to a scale 1:5000. This means that 1 cm on the map represents a distance of 5000 cm. A magnum of champagne is twice the volume of an ordinary bottle; their volumes are in the ratio 2:1. Two quantities of the same kind can always be compared in this manner.

Examples

1 A man is 45 years old, his son is 15 years old. Their ages are in the ratio 3:1.
2 The speed of a cyclist is 15 km/h, the speed of a car is 75 km/h. The ratio of their speeds is 1:5.
3 The price of a television licence was £5; it is now £60. The ratio of the old price to the new is 1:12.

It is always important that the order of the numbers is the same as the order of the items being compared. In **3** the ratio of the old price to the new is 1:12, the ratio of the new price to the old is 12:1.

Specimen question The sides of a triangle are in the ratio 2:3:4. Th perimeter is 18 cm. Find the length of each side.

Answer Since the sides are in the ratio 2:3:4, we must divide th perimeter into nine parts, each 2 cm long. Then the smallest side w have length two parts, i.e. 4 cm. Similarly the next side will hav length three parts, and the largest side four parts. The lengths a 4 cm, 6 cm, and 8 cm.

EXAMINATION QUESTIONS 5A

1   Three men form a syndicate for gambling. Their stakes one week ar £4.50, £3.60, £1.80. Express these as a ratio in its simplest terms.
2   A is twice as old as B, who is three times as old as C. Find the ratio o their ages.
3   Ann earns half as much as Beth; Beth earns three times as much a Chris. Find the ratio of their earnings.
4   Divide £5 between three friends in the ratio 2:3:5.
5   Three men invested £2000, £3000, and £4000 in a business. The prof each receives is proportional to the money invested. How much doe each receive when the total profits are £4500?
6   A sum of money is divided between three men, X, Y, and Z in th ratio 2:3:5. If Y receives £2.40 less then Z, how much does eac receive?

PERCENTAGES

Remember that percentages are merely fractions 'out of a hundred Thus 40% is $\frac{40}{100}$ and so 40% of £30 is:

$$\frac{40}{100} \times £30 = £12$$

To express 12 as a percentage of 60:

$$\frac{12}{60} \text{ is 12 as a fraction of 60}$$

and:

$$\frac{12}{60} \times 100 = 20$$

so that 12 is 20% of 60.

Specimen question Find 35% of £28.

Answer

$$\frac{35}{100} \times £28 = £9.80$$

Specimen question A driver stops for a rest when he has driven 180 km. If his total journey is 400 km, what percentage of his journey has he then covered?

Answer He has driven 180 km of a journey of 400km. This is $\frac{180}{400}$ of the journey, i.e.

$$\frac{180}{400} \times 100 = 45\% \text{ of the journey.}$$

EXAMINATION QUESTIONS 5B

1   Find:
   (a)   30% of 380
   (b)   35% of 38.5
   (c)   135% of £494
   (d) $66\frac{1}{2}\%$ of 54 km
2   Find:
   (a)   35% of $461, correct to the nearest $.
   (b)   38.5% of £54, correct to the nearest £.
   (c)   33.4% of 184 m, correct to the nearest cm.
3   Write:
   (a)   15 as a percentage of 60
   (b)   15 as a percentage of 80
   (c)   12.5 as a percentage of 250

PERCENTAGE CHANGE   Improvements to a railway line mean that my journey time of 3 hours is reduced by 10%, so that my new journey time is 90% of the old, i.e. 10% less. Since my old journey time was 3 hours, the new time is:

$$\frac{90}{100} \times 3 \text{ hours} = 2.7 \text{ hours} = 2 \text{ hours } 42 \text{ minutes}$$

Specimen question A woman grows vegetables in a rectangular plot of land, 30 m long by 12 m wide. She decides to increase the length of the plot by 20% and to decrease the width by 10%. What is the increase in the area of the land under vegetables? Express this as a percentage of the original vegetable plot.

Answer Since the length is increased by 20%, the new length is 120% of the old, i.e.

$$\frac{120}{100} \times 30 = 36 \text{ m}$$

Since the width is reduced by 10%, the new width is 90% of the old i.e.

$$\frac{90}{100} \times 12 = 10.8 \text{ m}$$

The new area is 36×10.8 m, i.e. 38.88 m², an increase of 2.88 m². To express this increase as a percentage of the original area, this is

$$\frac{2.88}{36} \times 100 = 8\%$$

TAXES

Many taxes are expressed in percentages. Income tax was 30% of taxable income for some people; VAT is 15% of the value of some goods; a duty may be levied on certain items, for example 20% of the value on spirits. Read the information in any such problem very carefully.

Specimen question If VAT is levied at 20%, find:
(a)   the total charge for a meal if the price before VAT was £16.50;
(b)   the price before VAT was added if the price with VAT is £20.40.

Answer
(a)   If VAT is levied at 20%, the price including VAT is 120% of £16.50, i.e.

$$\frac{120}{100} \times £16.50 = £19.80$$

(b)   Since the price with VAT is 120% of the initial price, £20.40 is 120% of the price before VAT. The price before VAT is thus:

$$\frac{100}{120} \times 20.40 = £17.00$$

Specimen question The length of a rectangle is increased by 20% and the breadth decreased by 20%. Find the percentage change in area.

Answer If the length of the rectangle was l units, a 20% increase is $\frac{20}{100}l$, and so the new length is $\frac{120}{100}l$ units. Similarly, if the breadth was b units, the new breadth is $\frac{80}{100}b$ units. The area was lb square units and is now:

$$\frac{120}{100}l \times \frac{80}{100}b = \frac{96}{100}lb \text{ square units}$$

so that the new area as a percentage of the old is:

$$\frac{\frac{96}{100}lb}{lb} \times 100 = 96\%, \text{ i.e. a decrease of } 4\%.$$

EXAMINATION QUESTIONS 5C

1 Find the new value when:
   (a)   42 is increased by 15%
   (b)   46 is decreased by 15%
   (c)   £40 is increased by $2\frac{1}{2}\%$
   (d)   400 grams is decreased by 5%
2 A factory reduces production costs by 5%. What is the new cost of an item previously costing £440 to make?
3 To buy a radio on hire purchase increases the cost by 30%. What is the hire purchase price of a radio costing £24 cash?
4 A car can be bought for a cash payment of £2400 or for a deposit of £780 and 12 payments of £185. What is the total credit cost of the deferred payment system? What is this as a percentage of the cash price? What percentage has been added to the cash price for giving credit?
5 When a girl's salary has been increased by 40% it is £4200. What was her salary before the increase?
6 A salesman receives commission of 4% of the value of the goods he sells. Calculate
   (a)   his commission when he sells goods value £48,
   (b)   the value of the goods he sold when he received £19.20 commission.
7 If x litres of antifreeze is poured into y litres of water, what percentage of the final mixture is water?
8 The VAT on a new lawnmower is £2.56, VAT being 8% of the original price. What was the original price of the lawnmower, and how much did the purchaser have to pay for the lawnmower?

PERCENTAGE PROFIT AND LOSS

If a dealer buys an article for £5 and sells it for £6 his profit is £1; this is one-fifth, i.e. 20%, of his outlay. Similarly, if he buys an article for £10 and sells it for £6 his loss, £4, is 40% of his outlay. In schools we always calculate the percentage profit or loss as a percentage of the outlay (**cost price**); commercial practice is different, shopkeepers finding it convenient to express their profit or loss as a percentage of their receipts (**selling price**).

If a trader sells an article at 20% profit, the selling price is 120% of the cost price; if he sells at 20% loss, the selling price is 80% of the cost price. More generally, when selling at $x\%$ profit:

$$\text{selling price} = \frac{100+x}{100}\, \text{cost price}$$

$$\text{cost price} = \frac{100}{100+x}\, \text{selling price}$$

When selling at x% loss:

$$\text{selling price} = \frac{100-x}{100}\, \text{cost price}$$

$$\text{cost price} = \frac{100}{100-x}\, \text{selling price}$$

For practice, copy and complete Table 5.1.

Table 5.1

Cost price (outlay)	% profit (or loss)	Multiplying factor	Profit or loss	Selling price
£60	40%	$\frac{140}{100}$		
£80			£20	
			£25	£75
	60%	$\frac{100}{60}$		£80
	30%		£15	
£60				£75

Although profit and loss are the simplest percentage changes made in a quantity, many other changes can be expressed as percentages of the original quantity. The extension in a bar when heated may be a percentage of the unheated length of the bar; the change in volume when chemicals are mixed may be a percentage of the total volume of the chemicals being mixed. The error in a faulty speedometer may indicate a speed a certain percentage more (or less) than the correct speed.

Specimen question The population of a certain town increases each year by 10% of the population at the beginning of that year. The population at the beginning of 1978 was 66 000. Calculate the population
(*a*)   at the beginning of 1977,
(*b*)   at the beginning of 1979.

Answer
(*a*)   The population in 1978 is 10% more than the population in 1977, i.e. the population in 1978 is 110% of the population in 1977. As the population in 1978 is 66 000, the population in 1977 was:

$$\tfrac{100}{110} \times 66\,000 = 60\,000$$

(*b*)   The population in 1979 is 110% of the population in 1978, so the population in 1979 is:

$$\tfrac{110}{100} \times 66\,000 = 72\,600$$

1 Calculate 40% of 320.

2 40% of a certain number is 320. What is the original number?

3 Improvements in a factory production line mean that the time taken on any task is reduced by 25%.
(a) What is the reduction in time of a task that used to take 6 minutes?
(b) How long does a task take that used to take 8 minutes?
(c) To fit a particular part now takes 135 seconds. How long did it take originally?

4 In a sale, all prices are reduced by 10%.
(a) What is the sale price of a book marked originally at £6?
(b) What was the original price of a camera if the sale price is £18?
(c) What was the original price of a flask which had a 40p reduction in the sale?
(d) What was the reduction in price of a bowl whose sale price was £6.30?

5 Only 64% of the voters in a constituency of 45 000 actually voted. Of the votes cast, candidate A received 40%, candidate B received 22%, and candidate C the remainder. How many votes did C receive?

6 In a school of 700 boys, every boy plays football or hockey or both. 74% play football and 66% play hockey. How many boys play both?

7 One year the taxable income of a certain man was £7600. He paid tax at 33% on the first £5000, 43% on the next £1000, and 50% on the remainder. How much tax did he pay that year?

8 In the same year, his friend had a taxable income of £5850. How much tax did he have to pay?

SIMPLE AND COMPOUND INTEREST

CONTENTS

▶ Summary   67

▶ Simple interest   67

▶ Compound interest   68

▶ Examination questions 6   68

SUMMARY

♦ The **simple interest** I on a loan or investment (the principal) P for T years at $R\%$ per annum (pa) is given by:

$$I = \frac{PRT}{100}$$

♦ The **compound interest** is $A - P$, where A is the amount and:

$$A = P\left(1 + \frac{R}{100}\right)^T$$

NB Remember to subtract from A the principal P to find the **interest**.

SIMPLE INTEREST

When money is saved and invested, the investor receives some **interest** each year, which is often a fixed percentage of the money invested (the **principal**). If the interest agreed is 5%, then for an investment of £400, the saver would have received £20 per year (pa for per annum). If the money was invested for 5 years, he would receive £20 each year, a total of £100.

If £P is invested for T years at R per cent per annum, then the interest £I is given by:

$$I = \frac{PRT}{100}$$

This formula can be transposed to give:

$$T = \frac{100I}{PR}; \quad R = \frac{100I}{PT}; \quad \text{and } P = \frac{100I}{RT}$$

if we know the interest earned and wish to find one of the other quantities.

Specimen question Find the (simple) interest on a loan of £480 for 4 years at 7½% pa.

Answer Write the $7\frac{1}{2}$ as $\frac{15}{2}$. Then the interest in £ is:

$$\frac{480 \times 4 \times 15}{100 \times 2} = £144.00$$

COMPOUND INTEREST

If, instead of drawing the interest each year, we leave it to increase the value of the savings, then we have more and more money invested each year, and so more and more interest is earned each year. This is called compound interest.

If £200 is invested at 8% pa compound interest, we can set out the calculations to find the value of the investment after three years like this:

Principal initially	£200.00
Interest for 1st year, 8% of £200	16.00
Principal for 2nd year	216.00
Interest for 2nd year, 8% of £216	17.28
Principal for 3rd year	233.28
Interest for 3rd year, 8% of £233.28	18.66 (correct to the nearest penny)
Amount after three years	£251.94

Working the same problem algebraically, with principal £P invested at R% pa for T years, the amount £A is given by the formula:

$$A = P\left(1 + \frac{R}{100}\right)^T$$

Using this formula in the example gives:

$$A = 200 \, (1.08)^3$$
$$= 251.94, \text{ correct to two decimal places}$$

The amount invested is £251.94; the interest that has been earned is £51.94

NB To find the interest, remember to subtract the principal from the amount.

EXAMINATION QUESTIONS 6

1   Find the simple interest on £680 for 5 years at 5% pa.
2   Find the simple interest on £48 for $2\frac{1}{2}$ years at $7\frac{1}{2}$% pa
3   Find the simple interest on £640 for 5 months at 6% pa.
4   Find the simple interest, correct to the nearest £, on:
   (a)   £860 for $5\frac{1}{2}$ years at $8\frac{1}{2}$% pa;
   (b)   £57.40 for 12 years at 5% pa;
   (c)   £360 for 2 years 8 months at 8% pa.
5   If the simple interest on £280 borrowed for 4 years is £39.20, at what rate per cent per annum has interest been charged?
6   If the simple interest on a loan of £2200 at 8% is £44, for how long has the money been borrowed?

7   If the simple interest on a loan at 3% pa for $2\frac{1}{2}$ years is £120, how much money was borrowed?

8   A loan of £120 was completely discharged after two years by a payment of £134.40, i.e. £134.40 repaid the principal and the interest due. At what rate per cent per annum was interest charged?

9   A loan of £250 was completely discharged by a payment of £375 after 4 years. At what rate per cent per annum had the interest been charged?

10 A man borrowed £5000 on 1 January 1974. He undertook to repay £1000 on 1 January 1975 and each succeeding year until the debt was repaid. Interest at 8% of the amount outstanding each year was added at the end of each year. How much was owing at the end of 1974, 1975, 1976 and 1977?

11 A man invested £500 on 1 January 1977, £1000 on 1 January 1978 and £500 on 1 January 1979. Interest at 8% of the amount to his credit was added at the end of each year. If the man did not make any withdrawals, how much had he to his credit at the end of 1979, when interest for that year had been added?

12 Find the compound interest on a loan of:
    (a)   £600 for 4 years at 5% pa;
    (b)   £400 for 3 years at 8% pa;
    (c)   £800 for 10 years at 10% pa;
    (d)   £1000 for 14 years at 5% pa.

UNITS; AREA AND VOLUME; SIMILARITY; ACCURACY

CONTENTS

▶ **Summary**   73

▶ **Length**   74

▶ **Area**   75
Areas of similar figures   75

▶ **Scales and scale-factors**   75

▶ **Volumes of similar solids**   76

▶ **Examination questions 7**   77

SUMMARY

♦ Metric (SI) measures of length:

    1 km (kilometre) = 1000 m (metres)

    1 m   = 100 cm (centimetres)

                 = 1000 mm (millimetres)

♦ Metric (SI) measures of area:

    1 hectare   = $10\,000^2$ (square metres)   = $10^4\,m^2$

    $1\,m^2$ = $10\,000\,cm^2$ (square centimetres)   = $10^4\,cm^2$

♦ Metric (SI) measures of volume:

    $1\,m^3$ = $1\,000\,000\,cm^3$ (cubic centimetres) = $10^6\,cm^3$

    1 litre   = $1000\,cm^3$

♦ The area of a triangle (Fig. 7.1) is:

$$\tfrac{1}{2}\,base \times perpendicular\ height = \tfrac{1}{2}bh$$

♦ The area of a trapezium (Fig. 7.2) is:

$\tfrac{1}{2}$ (sum of the parallel sides) × perpendicular distance between them

$= \tfrac{1}{2}(a+b) \times h$

♦ The circumference of a circle is $2\pi r$.

♦ The area of a circle is πr^2.

Fig. 7.1

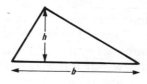

Fig. 7.2

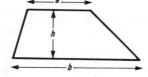

Fig. 7.3

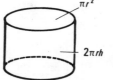

- The curved surface area of a cylinder (Fig. 7.3) is $2\pi rh$.
- The area of one end of a cylinder is πr^2.
- The volume of a cylinder is $\pi r^2 h$.
- The curved surface area of a sphere is $4\pi r^2$.
- The volume of a sphere is $\frac{4}{3}\pi r^3$.
- The volume of a cone is $\frac{1}{3}\pi r^2 h$.
- If two figures have lengths in the ratio 1:k, (scale factor, k) corresponding areas are in the ratio 1:k^2 and corresponding volumes 1:k^3.
- The most useful relations between areas are:

$$1\,m^2 = 1\,000\,000\,mm^2 \; (10^6\,mm^2)$$
$$1\,m^2 = 10\,000\,cm^2 \; (10^4\,cm^2)$$
$$1\,km^2 = 1\,000\,000\,m^2 \; (10^6\,m^2)$$

- The area of a square 100 m by 100 m is called a hectare, so that:

$$1\,hectare\,(1\,ha) = 10^4\,m^2$$

- The area of a full-sized football pitch is just under 1 hectare.
- The unit of volume is the cubic m (m^3), the volume of a cube edge 1 m. As with area, since 1 m = 100 cm, the volume of the cube is also $100 \times 100 \times 100$ cm^3, so that:

$$1\,m^3 = 1\,000\,000\,cm^3$$

- The most useful relations between volumes are:

$$1\,m^3 = 1\,000\,000\,000\,mm^3 \; (10^9\,mm^3)$$
$$1\,m^3 = 1\,000\,000\,cm^3 \; (10^6\,cm^3)$$

- 1 litre can be taken to be 1000 cm^3.

NB Always draw a clear figure to illustrate each question.

LENGTH

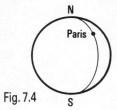

Fig. 7.4

The SI (Système Internationale) unit of length is the metre, about the length of the stride of a tall man. The metre was first defined as one quarter of the ten-millionth part of the great circle through Paris (Fig. 7.4); the measurement on which this was based later proved inaccurate, and the metre has now been redefined, to the satisfaction of scientists and others, in terms of the wave-length of orange light from krypton.

A metre is inconveniently large for some measurements and too small for others, so that multiples and fractions of the metre are used. The most useful are:

$$\begin{aligned}
1 \text{ kilometre (km)} &= 1000 \text{ metres (m)} \\
100 \text{ centimetres (cm)} &= 1 \text{ metre} \\
1000 \text{ millimetres (mm)} &= 1 \text{ metre}
\end{aligned}$$

AREA

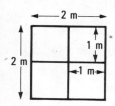

Fig. 7.5

A square, side 2 m, can be divided into four smaller squares, each side 1 m, and we see that the area of the square is 4 square metres (m^2) (Fig 7.5).

Similarly, a square 1 m by 1 m (with area 1 m^2) can be thought of as a square 100 cm by 100 cm, area 10 000 cm^2, so that:

$$1 \ m^2 = 10\,000 \ cm^2$$

Specimen question A circular washer is bounded by concentric circles, radii R cm and r cm. Find the surface area of one side of the washer if
(a) $R = 5$ and $r = 3$,
(b) $R = 5.4$ and $r = 3.2$.

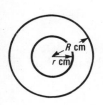

Fig. 7.6

Answer Draw Fig. 7.6. The surface area A cm^2 is the difference between two circles, i.e. $\pi R^2 - \pi r^2$

In (a) $A = \pi \times 5^2 - \pi \times 3^2$; simple numbers like these suggest that a calculator should not be used, so that:

$$A = 25\pi - 9\pi$$
$$= 16\pi$$
$$= 50.24 \ cm, \text{ taking } \pi \text{ to be } 3.14$$

The area is 50.24 cm^2.
In (b) it will be quicker to use a calculator, so:
$$A = \pi \times (5.4)^2 - \pi \times (3.2)^2$$
$$\triangle \ 59.439$$

The area is approximately 59.4 cm^2.

AREAS OF SIMILAR FIGURES

The areas of similar figures are in the ratio of the squares of their corresponding linear dimensions. If the radius of one circle is twice that of another, their areas are in the ratio 4:1. If the sides of similar triangles are in the ratio 2:3, their areas are in the ratio 4:9. If a model of a railway locomotive is made on a scale of 1:20, the surface area of the locomotive is 400 times that of the model.

SCALES AND SCALE-FACTORS

If the scale of a map is 1:1000, then each line on the map will be one-thousandth of the line that it represents. A region on the map will be of the same shape as the region that it represents, and so the ratio of the areas will be 1:1000^2 m that is, 1:1 000 000.

When solving scale problems, always draw two diagrams, one showing the scale figure, one the figure that it represents.

Specimen question A map (Fig. 7.7(*a*)), scale 1:5000 shows a field represented by a rectangle ABCD, with AB = 5 cm and BC = 8 cm. A straight footpath goes from the corner represented by A to the midpoint of the opposite side. Find

(*a*)   the length of the footpath,

(*b*)   the area of the triangular part of the field, one side of which is the footpath.

Fig. 7.7

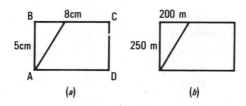

(*a*)

(*b*)

Answer Since the scale is 1:5000, 1 cm on the map represents 50 m.

(*a*)   By Pythagoras' theorem, using Fig. 7.7(*b*), the length of the footpath is $\sqrt{(200^2+250^2)}$, i.e. approximately 320 m.

(*b*)   The area of the trangular region is:

$$\tfrac{1}{2}\text{base}\times\text{height} = \tfrac{1}{2}\times200\times250 \text{ m}^2$$
$$= 25\,000 \text{ m}^2$$

VOLUMES OF SIMILAR SOLIDS

Volumes of similar solids are in the ratio of the cubes of their corresponding linear dimensions. If a radius of a sphere is doubled, its volume is increased by a factor of 8. If the heights of two cones are in the ratio 2:3, their volumes are in the ratio 8:27, if the shapes of the cones are the same.

Specimen question A cone height 10 cm is cut by a plane parallel to its base, 4 cm from that base. Find the ratio of

(*a*)   the surface areas,

(*b*)   the volumes,

of the smaller cone to the larger one.

Fig. 7.8

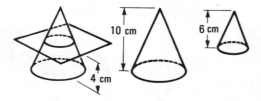

Answer Since the plane is 4 cm from the base, the height of the smaller cone is 6 cm (Fig. 7.8). Since the smaller cone is formed from the larger cone, they are of the same shape, so that:

(a)   the areas are in the ratio $6^2:10^2$, i.e. 9:25;
(b)   the volumes are in the ratio $6^3:10^3$, i.e. 27:125.

EXAMINATION QUESTIONS 7

These questions should be answered without using a calculator.

1   Find the area of a rectangle, sides
  (a)   2.4 cm by 7 cm,
  (b)   3.5 cm by 8 cm.

2   Find the length of a rectangle, given that
  (a)   the area is 40 cm^2 and the breadth is 2.5 cm,
  (b)   the area is 640 cm^2 and the breadth is 8 cm.

3   A certain map has a scale of 1:50 000
  (a)   What is the length represented by a line 3 cm on the map?
  (b)   What length on the map represents a distance of 2 km?
  (c)   What is the area of the region represented on the map by a square, area 4 cm^2?
  (d)   What area on the map represents 4 km^2?

4   A model, scale factor 1:20, is made of a house. Write down the ratio of:
  (a)   a length of piping in the model to that in the house;
  (b)   the area of a window in the model to that in the house;
  (c)   the volume of a room in the model to that in the house.

ESTIMATION AND APPROXIMATION

CONTENTS

▶ **Summary** 81

▶ **Estimation** 81
Familiarity with common objects 81
Accuracy of estimates 82

▶ **Examination questions 8A** 82
Mass 83

▶ **Examination questions 8B** 83

SUMMARY

- Notice the size of common objects.
- A man of average height is about 1.75 metres, i.e. 175 cm, tall.
- His foot, in a shoe, will be about 30 cm long.
- A packet of tea, common size, is 200 grams, but make a habit of looking at the mass printed on all packets.
- A man walks at about 6 kilometres an hour; he takes about 1 minute to walk 100 metres.
- Look at the length of a 100 m athletics track; it is a useful guide for judging distances.

ESTIMATION

Although the information in any problem will often have been obtained by measurement, we ought to be able to make good estimates of the quantities we are handling to enable us to tackle a problem efficiently and to see whether our answer is reasonable. For example, to find the distance travelled by a car in 2 hours, we would expect the car to travel 'about' 80 miles or 'about' 120 kilometres, because cars usually travel between about 30 mph and 70 mph (50 kph and 110 kph) unless their speed is restricted by traffic in towns.

FAMILIARITY WITH COMMON OBJECTS

Some of the difficulty that we have in making estimates may be because we still use Imperial units – feet, miles, etc. – as well as SI units – metres, kilograms, etc. Whereas the Imperial units were based on objects in common use, e.g. a foot was the length of a foot, a yard was a good stride or pace, the SI units were designed for the convenience of scientists. However, the following rough estimates may help.

- The height of a tall man is about 6 feet or 2 yards or 1.8 metres.
- His span is roughly equal to his height (Fig. 8.1).
- The length of a fairly large man's shoe is 1 foot (12 inches) or 30 centimetres.
- The span of a hand is about 8 inches or 20 cm (Fig. 8.2).
- The top joint of a thumb is about 1 inch or 2 to 3 cm (Fig. 8.3).
- A fairly fast walking speed is 4 miles per hour – about 6 kilometres per hour.

Fig. 8.1

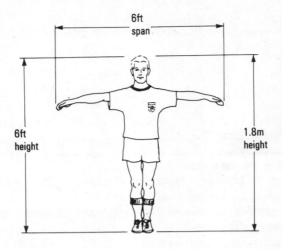

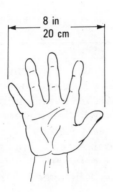

Fig. 8.2

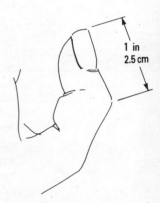

Fig. 8.3

- A good school athlete will run a middle-distance race at about 12 miles per hour or 20 kilometres per hour.
- The athlete will reach a speed of over 30 kilometres per hour (about 20 mph) in the 100-metre race, but for a short distance like that it is more appropriate to estimate his speed in metres and seconds, say about 10 metres per second (about 30 feet per second).

ACCURACY OF ESTIMATES

We should only try to obtain the correct order of size of our estimates; do not worry about being very accurate.

Because of the great variations in size of many objects, estimation may be tested in the oral test (where that is part of the examination procedure).

1   Estimate the following.
    (a)   The length of a bicycle.
    (b)   The speed of a commercial aircraft.
    (c)   The speed of a race horse.
    (d)   The distance from Dover to Calais.
    (e)   The distance over the surface of the earth from London to Paris.

2   Estimate the following.
    (a)   The height above the floor of a dining table.
    (b)   The length and breadth of a bath.
    (c)   The capacity, in cubic centimetres, of a bottle of fruit squash.
    (d)   The length, breadth and height of a pack of butter.
    (e)   The volume in cubic centimetres of a cup of tea.

3   Which of the following is NOT likely to be the length of a car?
    (a)   1.5 m
    (b)   4.5 m
    (c)   15 m

4   Which of the following might be the length of a car?
    (a)   450 cm
    (b)   150 cm
    (c)   15 000 cm

5   Which of the following are NOT likely to be the height and width of a door in an ordinary house?
    (a)   150 cm by 90 cm
    (b)   230 cm by 90 cm
    (c)   170 cm by 150 cm
    (d)   340 cm by 250 cm

MASS

Mass and weight are more difficult to estimate, partly because the same Imperial unit (the pound, lb) was used for both mass and weight. The SI unit of mass is the kilogram (kg). Note the mass of familiar objects.

▸ The mass of the commonest pack of butter is 250 grams.
▸ The mass of a large packet of cornflakes is 500 grams.
▸ The mass of a sack of potatoes is 25 kg.
▸ The mass of a medium-size family saloon car is about 800 kg.

1   Estimate the mass of the following.
    (a)   A bottle of milk.
    (b)   A carton of tea.
    (c)   A very fit adult man of average height.
    (d)   A man who overeats, drinks too much and takes no exercise.
    (e)   An electric locomotive.

STATISTICS AND THE REPRESENTATION OF DATA

CONTENTS

▶ **Summary** 87

▶ **Average** 87
Mean 88
Median 88
Mode 89

▶ **Examination questions 9A** 89

▶ **Frequency distribution** 89
Cumulative frequency curve 91

▶ **Examination questions 9B** 92

▶ **Representation of data** 93
Pie chart 93
Histogram 94

▶ **Misrepresentation of data** 95

▶ **Examination questions 9C** 96

SUMMARY

Fig. 9.1

♦ To find the **mean** of n scores, add them together and divide by n, e.g. the mean of 1, 5, 6 is $(1+5+6) \div 3 = 4$.

♦ The **median** is the middle score when arranged in ascending order, e.g.
the median of 1, 6, 5 is 5;
the median of 1, 6, 5, 4 is $(4+5) \div 2 = 4\frac{1}{2}$.

♦ The **mode** is the commonest score, e.g. the mode of 2, 3, 1, 3 is 3.

♦ In a **pie chart** the angle at the centre of the circle is proportional to the frequency (see Fig.9.1).

♦ In a **histogram** the *area* of each rectangle is proportional to the frequency. Check the widths of the rectangle, as in Fig. 9.2.

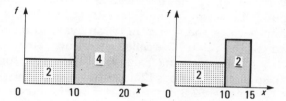

Fig. 9.2

♦ The **cumulative frequency curve** gives the cumulative frequency less than (or less than or equal to) a certain score. Check whether a question requires a reading *less* than or *greater* than a certain score. The median of n scores is found by reading against the cumulative frequency of $\frac{1}{2}(n+1)$ (Fig. 9.3); if n is large, $\frac{1}{2}n$ may be used.

Fig. 9.3

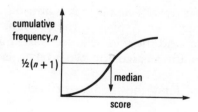

AVERAGE

'The average industrial wage is now £84.90 a week' . . . 'His average score last cricket season was 24.9 runs' . . . We know that some workers earned less than £84.90 a week, and that some eaned more; we know that this batsman certainly did not score 24.9 runs in any innings, let alone every innings. These numbers are merely **statistics** which, interpreted correctly, tell us something about the industrial earnings or something about the number of runs scored by this batsman.

MEAN

The commonest way of finding a statistic to give information about a sample is to add all the elements in the sample together, and to divide by the number of elements in that sample. This is the statistic used when giving the batting 'average' of cricketers, the 'average' number of goals scored in each football match, and it is called the **mean**.

Specimen question Find the mean of each of the following sets of scores:
(*a*)　　1, 1, 2, 4, 5, 5, 6, 6, 7, 7
(*b*)　　1.2, 1.2, 2.2, 4.2, 5.2, 5.2, 6.2, 6.2, 7.2, 7.2
(*c*)　　12, 12, 24, 48, 60, 60, 72, 72, 84, 84

Answer
(*a*)　　Since the sum of the ten scores 1, 1, 2, 4, 5, 5, 6, 6, 7, 7 is 44, the mean is $\frac{44}{10}$, i.e. 4.4.
(*b*)　　The scores in (*b*) are each 0.2 more than the corresponding scores in (*a*), so that the mean is 4.4+0.2, i.e. 4.6. If we had not first found the mean of the scores in (*a*), we could have subtracted 0.2 from each of the scores in (*b*) anyway, to enable us to use simpler scores. The value 0.2 is called a **working zero**.
(*c*)　　The scores in (*c*) are each 12 times the corresponding scores in (*a*), so that the mean is 12 times the mean of the scores in (*a*); the mean is 12×4.4, i.e. 52.8. If we had not first found the mean of the scores in (*a*), we could still have noticed that we had a common factor of 12, and so could have divided each score by 12, and used the simpler scores, 1, 1, 2, 4, etc. The number 12 is called a **scaling factor**.

MEDIAN

A statistic that is not affected by a few unusual scores of extreme size, either very large or very small, is the **median**. The scores are ranked in order of size, and the middle score is the median. If there are two 'middle' scores, the mean of the two is taken as the median.

Specimen question Find the median of each of the following sets of scores:
(*a*)　　0, 1, 0, 2, 5, 0, 4;
(*b*)　　0, 1, 0, 2, 5, 0, 4, 3.

Answer Rearranging the scores in (*a*) in ascending order, we have:

$$0, 0, 0, \boxed{1}, 2, 4, 5$$
$$\downarrow$$
$$\text{median}$$

The middle one of these is 1, so the median is 1.

When we rearrange the scores in (b), we have:

0, 0, 0, $\boxed{1, 2}$, 3, 4, 5

median is $\dfrac{1+2}{2}$

There are eight scores now, so the median is the mean of 1 and 2, i.e. 1.5.

MODE

A third term that is sometimes used to describe a number of scores is the **mode**; this is merely the commonest, the score that occurs most frequently, e.g. the mode of 0, 1, 0, 2, 0, 1, 2, 1, 3, 0 is 0.

EXAMINATION QUESTIONS 9A

1   Find the mean, median, and mode of each of the following sets of scores:
(a)   2, 2, 3, 4, 6
(b)   1, 1, 2, 3, 5, 6
(c)   1, 0, 1, 4, 2, 3
(d   1, 0, 2, 0, 5, 7

2   Find the mean of the following sets of scores:
(a)   1, 1, 3, 5, 7
(b)   0.1, 0.1, 0.3, 0.5, 0.7
(c)   21, 21, 23, 25, 27
(d)   981, 981, 983, 985, 987

3   Find x if the mean of 1, 3, 6, 7 and x is 4.

4   The mean of ten scores is 4. If six of these scores have a mean of 6, find the mean of the other four scores.

FREQUENCY DISTRIBUTION

Consider the scores 1, 1, 1, 1, 2, 2, 2, 3, 4, 4, 4, 4.

To find their mean, we could add all together and divide by 12. We can say that the **frequency** of 1 is four, since there are four scores of 1; that the frequency of 2 is three, since there are three scores of 2; and so on. For large numbers of scores it often helps to make out a frequency table as in Table 9.1.

The total number of scores is the sum of the frequencies, i.e. 50. The sum of all the scores is the total in the third column, i.e. 641, so the mean is $641 \div 50$, i.e. 12.82.

We may have the frequency of scores in certain **intervals** given, as in the following example.

Table 9.1 A frequency table

scores (x)	frequency (f)	Product (fx)
11	9	99
12	15	180
13	11	143
14	8	112
15	5	75
16	2	32
	50	641

Specimen question A survey taken one day showed the following annual salaries of a sample of travellers at a certain railway station.

£5000 or above, and below £6000	7
£6000 or above, and below £7000	13
£7000 or above, and below £8000	16
£8000 or above, and below £9000	9
£9000 or above, and below £10 000	5

Use mid-interval values to estimate the mean annual salary of these travellers.

Answer Since we do not know the exact salary of these travellers, we estimate that those travellers with salaries between £5000 and £6000 have a salary of £5500, those in the range £6000–£7000 have a salary of £6500, and so on. Using a working zero of £5500 simplifies the calculations a little, and the calculations should be set out as in Table 9.2.

Table 9.2

Score (£x)	£(x−5500)	f	f(x−5500)
5500	0	7	0
6500	1000	13	13 000
7500	2000	16	32 000
8500	3000	9	27 000
9500	4000	5	20 000
		50	92 000

$$\frac{92\,000}{50} = 1840$$

so the mean is 1840 greater than the working zero, i.e. 5500+1840; the mean salary is thus £7340.

Notice that if we have been given open intervals, 'below £5000' or 'above £10 000', we should not have known from the data what to take as a mid-interval value, and should have not been able to calculate an estimate of the mean. Sometimes, though, our general knowledge may help to suggest likely boundaries, e.g. speeds of cars on roads rarely exceed 110 km h⁻¹.

CUMULATIVE FREQUENCY CURVE

Looking at the data in the preceding specimen question, we see that:

no traveller had a salary of less than	£5000 pa
7 travellers had a salary of less than	£6000 pa
20 travellers had a salary of less than	£7000 pa
36 travellers had a salary of less than	£8000 pa
45 travellers had a salary of less than	£9000 pa
50 travellers had a salary of less than	£10 000 pa

The figures in the left-hand column are the **cumulative** sums of the frequencies and the curve displaying these is called a cumulative frequency curve (Fig. 9.4).

Fig. 9.4

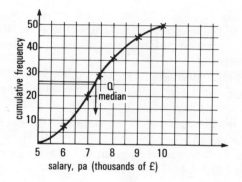

We usually join the points we have plotted by a smooth curve; if a series of straight lines is used, giving a cumulative frequency diagram, that assumes the salaries are evenly spread over each interval, whereas we might expect that of the nine travellers with salaries in the range £8000–£9000, more than half would have a salary nearer to £8000 than to £9000.

Using our cumulative frequency curve, we can estimate that 15 travellers had a salary below £6600, in particular that half the travellers had a salary below £7300. This last estimate suggests that the median will be about £7300. Strictly, as we have 50 scores, the median is between the 25th and the 26th score, but with larger samples than this, e.g. 500 scores, the difference is negligible and we can read the halfway score as the median.

Specimen question Only travellers earning more than £7500 can join the Luncheon Club. How many travellers are eligible to join?

Answer Reading across at Q in Fig. 9.4, we have the cumulative frequency of 29. This tells us that 29 travellers earn below £7500, so that 21 will earn above. Thus 21 travellers can belong to the Luncheon Club.

NB Always note whether readings *above* or *below* a given value are required. To pass an examination, candidates have to score *more* than a certain mark; if eggs are to be graded as large, their mass has to be *greater* than a given mass; to be graded as small, their mass has to be *less* than a given mass.

EXAMINATION QUESTIONS 9B

1   The marks of 500 candidates in a GCSE examination are given in Table 9.3.

Table 9.3

Marks	0–9	10–19	20–29	30–39	40–49	50–59	60–69	70–79	80–89	90–99
Number of candidates	8	17	28	38	60	78	110	70	54	37

(*a*)   Taking mid-interval values of 4.5, 14.5, etc., calculate an estimate of the mean mark scored by these candidates.
(*b*)   Draw a cumulative frequency curve for this distribution and use it to estimate:
  (i) the median mark;
  (ii) the mark exceeded by 30% of these candidates (called the 30th percentile);
  (iii) the number of candidates who passed, if the pass mark was 44%.

2   A certain firm recorded the number of letters posted each day over a period of 100 days (Table 9.4).

Table 9.4

Number of letters	0–19	20–29	30–39	40–49	50–59
Number of days	9	23	38	27	3

(*a*)   Taking mid-interval values of 9.5, 24.5, 34.5, etc., calculate an estimate of the mean number of letters posted in a day.
(*b*)   Draw a cumulative frequency curve for this distribution and estimate:
  (i) the median number of letters posted in one day;
  (ii) on how many days more than 45 letters were posted.

REPRESENTATION OF DATA

PIE CHART

When data has been collected, we may wish to use a diagram to display this data in a clear and attractive manner, as in Fig. 9.5, which displays famous data collected by *The Economist* to show that transport, both public and private, is used more by the richer socio-economic groups than by the poorer, perhaps suggesting that transport subsidies help mainly the rich. These diagrams are called pie charts or, sometimes, circular diagrams. Since the area of each section is proportional to the angle of the centre of the circle, the ratio of the angles is made equal to the ratio of the quantities displayed in the diagram. This diagram represents most clearly different proportions of a whole, e.g. the number of lessons a week spent on each subject in school, the fractions of an income spent on rent, food, clothing, etc.

Fig. 9.5

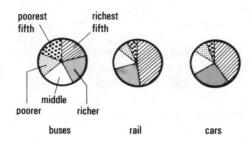

poorest fifth — richest fifth — middle — poorer — richer

buses — rail — cars

Specimen question A consumer agency noted that in one year 500 of its callers complained once, 200 complained twice, 50 complained three times, 50 complained four times, and 100 complained five or more times. Draw a pie chart to display this data.

Answer There were 900 callers at this agency, so that:

900 callers will be represented by 360°

500 callers by $\frac{500}{900} \times 360°$, i.e. by 200°

200 callers by $\frac{200}{900} \times 360°$, i.e. by 80°

50 callers by $\frac{50}{900} \times 360°$, i.e. by 20°

50 callers by $\frac{50}{900} \times 360°$, i.e. by 20°

100 callers by $\frac{100}{900} \times 360°$, i.e. by 40°

$$\overline{360°}$$

Check: Total of 900 callers.

Draw a sector of a circle, angle 200°, another angle 80°, and so on, and mark the diagram as in Fig. 9.6.

Fig. 9.6

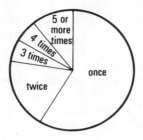

HISTOGRAM

Probably the commonest type of diagram is like Fig. 9.7, which shows the assets of a small building society. The area of each rectangle is proportional to the amount of money it represents. If the *rectangles are of equal width*, as is often the case, then the length of each rectangle will be proportional to the amount represented. This must not make us think that the length is *always* proportional to the amount represented. Check carefully whether the class intervals have the same width. It may well be realistic to have class intervals of different widths and many GCSE questions on histograms test this.

Fig. 9.7

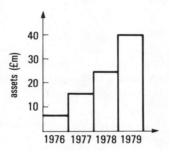

Specimen question A sample of 100 drivers were asked how far they were planning to drive on that journey, and their replies recorded in Table 9.5. Draw a histogram to represent this data.

Table 9.5

Distance	Less than 5 km	5 km– 10 km	10 km– 20 km	20 km– 30 km	30 km– 40 km
Number of drivers	4	16	16	24	40

Answer Notice that the first two class intervals are of width 5 km, the others of width 10 km. In Fig. 9.8, if we mark the x-axis as shown and take a scale of 2 cm to represent 10 cars in each of the first two intervals, then 2 cm of length will represent 20 cars in each of the other intervals. Notice in particular that since the intervals 5 km–10 km and 10 km–20 km have the same number of drivers, they must be represented by rectangles of the same area.

Fig. 9.8

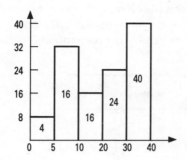

MISREPRESENTATION OF DATA

From time to time one sees data that is misrepresented, e.g. represented by diagrams that distort the data. Common ways of distorting data are using a false origin (Fig. 9.9), or by using areas or volumes instead of lengths. In Fig. 9.10, the length of each loaf is proportional to the price, but the eye compares the volumes of the loaves.

Fig. 9.9

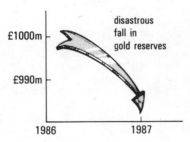

Fig. 9.10

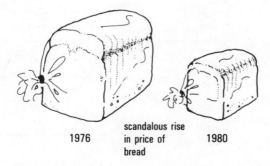

1 In 1987 a certain company analysed its fixed assets in different regions of the world: 33% of its assets were in Great Britain, 27% of its assets were in continental Europe, 25% in North America, and the rest were elsewhere. Draw a pie chart (circular diagram) to display this data.

2 A case of apples was opened and each apple weighed. The distribution of mass of the apples is given in Table 9.6.

Table 9.6

Mass in grams	Number of apples
60–100	40
100–120	40
120–140	20
140–160	30
160–200	30

Draw a histogram to display this data.

PROBABILITY

CONTENTS

▶	**Summary**	99
▶	**Definition**	99
▶	**Examination questions 10A**	100
▶	**Addition of probabilities**	100
▶	**Independent events** Product rule 101	101
▶	**Examination questions 10B**	103

- The **probability** of an outcome A:

$$p(A) = \frac{\text{Number of \textbf{equiprobable} favourable outcomes}}{\text{Total number of equiprobable outcomes}}$$

- If A and B denote two events:

$$p(A \text{ or } B \text{ or both}) = p(A) + p(B) - p(\text{both A and B})$$

- If A and B are two independent events:

$$p(A \text{ and } B) = p(A) \times p(B)$$

- Remember tree diagrams (pp.102–3) are often helpful.

We define the probability of an event as the ratio:

$$\frac{\text{The number of equiprobable favourable outcomes}}{\text{Total number of all equiprobable outcomes}}$$

For example:

- $p(\text{a fair die shows a '6'}) = \frac{1}{6}$

- $p(\text{a card drawn at random from a well-shuffled pack is a heart}) = \frac{13}{52}$

if there is not a joker in the pack. The probability is $\frac{13}{54}$ if there are two jokers, as there are now 54 equiprobable outcomes, although still only 13 are favourable. **But:**

- $p(\text{when two coins are thrown, both show heads})$ is **not** $\frac{1}{3}$

because the three outcomes 'two heads', 'one head and one tail' and 'two tails' are not equiprobable. The equiprobable outcomes are H H, H T, T H and T T, so that the probability that both coins show heads is $\frac{1}{4}$. For many simple probability questions, or in multiple-choice questions, it is sufficient to list all possible outcomes, and pick out those that are favourable.

Specimen question A number is selected at random from the integers 2 to 10 inclusive. Find the probability that the number chosen is (*a*) prime, (*b*) even, (*c*) a multiple of 3, (*d*) not a multiple of 3.

Answer The integers from 2 to 10 inclusive are 2, 3, 4, 5, 6, 7, 8, 9 and 10, and they can be called the **possibility set**, $\mathscr{E}$, of all possible outcomes.

In (*a*), the subject *A* of favourable outcomes is 2, 3, 5 and 7. Thus the probability that a number drawn chosen at random is prime is:

$$\frac{4}{9}, \quad \frac{n(A)}{n(\mathscr{E})}$$

In (*b*), the subset of favourable elements is 2, 4, 6, 8 and 10, so that:

$$p \text{ (number chosen at random is even)} = \tfrac{5}{9}$$

In (*c*), there are three multiples of three, 3, 6 and 9, so:

$$p \text{ (number chosen at random is a multiple of three)} = \tfrac{3}{9} = \tfrac{1}{3}$$

In (*d*), we can say that there are six numbers not multiples of three, so:

$$p \text{ (number chosen at random is not a multiple of three)} = \tfrac{6}{9} = \tfrac{2}{3}$$

Or we can say that either a number is a multiple of three or it is not a multiple of three, so that the probability that a number is a multiple of three is $1-\tfrac{1}{3}$, i.e. $\tfrac{2}{3}$

EXAMINATION QUESTIONS 10A

1   Four grey and three blue socks are in a laundry bag. If one is drawn at random, what is the probability that it is (*a*) grey, (*b*) blue?

2   *x* grey socks and *y* blue socks are in a laundry bag. If one is drawn at random, what is the probability that it is grey?

3   A letter is chosen at random from the letters LONDON. What is the probability that it is (*a*) L, (*b*) O?

4   A fair die has its faces marked 1, 1, 1, 2, 2 and 3. What is the probability that when thrown it shows a 1?

5   Assuming that a man is equally likely to be born on any day of the week, what is the probability that a man chosen at random was born on a Sunday?

ADDITION OF PROBABILITIES

What is the probability that a card drawn at random from a pack of 52 cards is either a king or a heart? There are 52 cards to choose from; of these 13 are hearts, 4 are kings, but one is the king of hearts, and so has been counted twice. There are just 16 favourable different equiprobable draws we can make, so the probability that a card is a king or a heart is:

$$\tfrac{16}{52} = \tfrac{4}{13}$$

Fig. 10.1

The relation between the cards can be illustrated by the Venn diagram in Fig. 10.1, where:

$$A = \{\text{all hearts}\} \text{ and } B = \{\text{all kings}\}$$

If $A \cup B$ is the set of all cards that are either hearts or kings or both, $A \cap B$ is the set of all cards that are both hearts and kings, i.e. the king of hearts, we have the rule:

$$p(A \cup B) = p(A) + p(B) - p(A \cap B)$$

It may prove difficult to remember the rule in this form, but drawing a Venn diagram prevents any element being counted more than once.

Specimen question Find the probability that a number chosen at random from the integers 2 to 10 inclusive is either a prime or a multiple of 3.

Answer If $A = \{\text{all primes}\}$, $B = \{\text{all multiples of 3}\}$, then the relation between the sets is illustrated in Fig. 10.2, and we see:

$$p(\text{number is either a prime or a multiple of 3}) = \tfrac{6}{9} = \tfrac{2}{3}$$

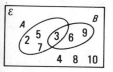

Fig. 10.2

INDEPENDENT EVENTS

Two events which are such that one has no effect on the other are called independent events. We usually assume events are independent unless there is a clear connection between them, such as drawing a heart from a pack of cards at the second draw; this may depend on whether we have drawn a heart at the first draw.

PRODUCT RULE

If we have two independent events A and B, then:

$$p(\text{both } A \text{ and } B) = p(A) \times p(B)$$

This rule is illustrated in the following two specimen questions.

Specimen question The coin is thrown four times. Find the probability that it shows four heads.

Answer

$p(\text{first throw shows heads}) \quad = \tfrac{1}{2}$
$p(\text{second throw shows heads}) = \tfrac{1}{2}$
$p(\text{third throw shows heads}) \quad = \tfrac{1}{2}$
$p(\text{fourth throw shows heads}) \quad = \tfrac{1}{2}$

Thus:

$p(\text{all four throws show heads}) = \tfrac{1}{2} \times \tfrac{1}{2} \times \tfrac{1}{2} \times \tfrac{1}{2} = \tfrac{1}{16}$

Specimen question The probability that an athlete A breaks the record of a race is $\tfrac{1}{2}$; the probability that an athlete B breaks the record in the same race is $\tfrac{1}{3}$. Find the probability that (a) both will break the record, (b) neither breaks the record.

Answer It might be argued by athletes that these probabilities are
dependent; that if A breaks the record, he will set a fast pace and so
might also break the record, but we have no information about the
manner in which they are dependent, so assume that the probabilities
are independent. Then:

$$p \text{ (A breaks the record)} = \tfrac{1}{2}$$
$$p \text{ (B breaks the record)} = \tfrac{1}{3}$$
$$p \text{ (A and B break the record)} = \tfrac{1}{2} \times \tfrac{1}{3} = \tfrac{1}{6}$$

Either A breaks the record or he does not break the record, so that:

$$p \text{ (A does not break the record)} = 1 - \tfrac{1}{2} = \tfrac{1}{2}$$
$$p \text{ (B does not break the record)} = 1 - \tfrac{1}{3} = \tfrac{2}{3}$$

therefore:

$$p \text{ (Neither A nor B breaks the record)} = \tfrac{1}{2} \times \tfrac{2}{3} = \tfrac{1}{3}$$

In slightly more difficult examples it is helpful to draw a tree diagram.

Specimen question A lecturer is supposed to give a course of four lectures; if he fails to give one, the lecture is given by his deputy. If the
lecturer gives one lecture, the probability that he will not give the next
is $\tfrac{3}{4}$; if he fails to give any one lecture, the probability that he will give
the next is $\tfrac{2}{3}$. He is certain to give the first lecture. Find the probability
that he (a) gives all four lectures; (b) gives the first and second but not
the third; (c) gives the third lecture; (d) gives the fourth lecture.

Fig. 10.3

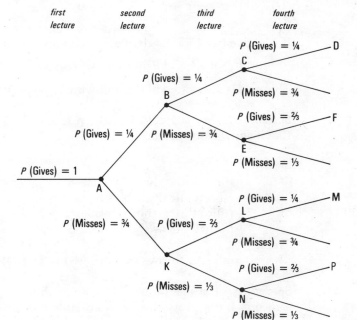

Answer Draw a tree diagram, as Fig. 10.3. We do not need to put in all the probabilities to answer these four questions, but they are inserted here to show the probability of each event, and the ease with which many other questions on this data can be answered. The probability that he gives all four lectures is found by reading A B C D, i.e.

$$p \text{ (gives all four lectures)} = 1 \times \tfrac{1}{4} \times \tfrac{1}{4} \times \tfrac{1}{4} = \tfrac{1}{64}$$

The probability that he gives the first and second lecture but not the third is found by reading A B E (notice that we are not interested whether he gives the fourth lecture or not), so:

$$p \text{ (he gives the first and second lectures but not the third)} = 1 \times \tfrac{1}{4} \times \tfrac{3}{4} = \tfrac{3}{16}$$

The probability that he gives the third lecture is found by reading A B C and A K L:

$$p \text{ (gives first, second, and third)} = 1 \times \tfrac{1}{4} \times \tfrac{1}{4} = \tfrac{1}{16}$$
$$p \text{ (gives first, not second, gives third)} = 1 \times \tfrac{3}{4} \times \tfrac{2}{3} = \tfrac{1}{2}$$

For either of these sequence of events, he gives the third lecture, so:

$$p \text{ (he gives the third lecture)} = \tfrac{1}{16} + \tfrac{1}{2} = \tfrac{9}{16}$$

The probability that he gives the fourth lecture is found by reading along the paths A B C D, A B E F, A K L M and A K N P. Thus:

$$p \text{ (gives the fourth lecture)} = \tfrac{1}{4} \times \tfrac{1}{4} \times \tfrac{1}{4} + \tfrac{1}{4} \times \tfrac{3}{4} \times \tfrac{2}{3} + \tfrac{3}{4} \times \tfrac{2}{3} \times \tfrac{1}{4} + \tfrac{3}{4} \times \tfrac{1}{3} \times \tfrac{2}{3}$$
$$= \tfrac{83}{192}$$

The working can be abbreviated by using $\tfrac{9}{16} \times \tfrac{1}{4} + \tfrac{7}{16} \times \tfrac{2}{3} = \tfrac{83}{192}$. Why?

EXAMINATION QUESTIONS 10B

1   A bag of sweets contains 7 toffees, 5 mints and 3 chocolates, all wrapped identically. Sweets are drawn out one at a time and not replaced. Find the probability that:
   (a)   the first drawn is a toffee;
   (b)   the first drawn is a toffee and the second a mint;
   (c)   the first and second drawn are both toffees;
   (d)   the second is a toffee;
   (e)   the third is a toffee;
   (f)   the fourth is a toffee.
   Guess the probability that when six of the sweets have been drawn, the next is a toffee.

2   A certain boy either walks to school or cycles. If he walks one day, the probability that he cycles the next is $\tfrac{4}{5}$; if he cycles one day, the probability that he walks the next is $\tfrac{2}{3}$. He walks to school on Monday of one week. Find the probability that during one week he:
   (a)   walks to school on both Tuesday and Wednesday;
   (b)   cycles on Tuesday and walks on Wednesday;
   (c)   walks on Wednesday;

(d)   cycles on Wednesday;

(e)   walks on Thursday;

(f)   walks every day that week.

3   In a game of tennis, after the score 'deuce' has been reached, either one player wins both the next two points, and then he wins the game; or each player wins one of the two points, and the score of 'deuce' is called again. In a certain game between two players A and B, the probability that A wins any one point is 0.7. Given that the score of deuce has just been reached, find the probability that:

(a)   A wins the next two points (and hence the game);

(b)   B wins the next two points (and hence the game);

(c)   each player wins one point, and so the score of deuce is called a second time;

(d)   the score of deuce is called a third time;

(e)   that after the score deuce is called a third time, A wins the match.

ALGEBRA

CONTENTS

Summary   107

Forming expressions   107
Evaluating expressions   108

Examination questions 11A   108

Common or 'shouting' factor   109

Examination questions 11B   109

Difference of two squares   109

Examination questions 11C   110

Trinominals   111

Examination questions 11D   111

Examination questions 11E   112

Grouping factors   113

Examination questions 11F   113

SUMMARY

- **Factors:**

$$ab+ac = a(b+c)$$
$$a^2-b^2 = (a-b)(a+b)$$
$$a^2-2ab+b^2 = (a-b)(a-b)$$

a^2+b^2 has no factors

- **Indices:**

$$a^m \times a^n = a^{m+n}, \text{ e.g. } a^2 \times a^3 = a^5$$
$$a^m \div a^n = a^{m-n}, \text{ e.g. } a^6 \div a^2 = a^4$$
$$(a^m)^n = a^{mn}$$
$$a^0 = 1$$
$$a^{-m} = \frac{1}{a^m}$$
$$a^{p/q} = \sqrt[q]{a^p}$$

- If a quadratic equation factorizes as $(x-a)(x+b) = 0$, the roots are $x = a$ or $-b$. *Note the change of signs.*

- If the quadratic equation $ax^2+bx+c = 0$ does not factorize easily, use the formula:

$$x = \frac{-b \pm \sqrt{b^2-4ac}}{2a}$$

- If $(x-a)(x-b)<0$ and $a<b$:

  $a<x<b$

- If $(x-a)(x-b)>0$ and $a<b$:

  $x<a$ or $b<x$

FORMING EXPRESSIONS

In algebra we use letters to denote numbers, so that the letters are, in general, subject to the ordinary rules of arithmetic. For example, if x denotes any one number:

$x+3$ is the number 3 larger than the first number;

$\frac{1}{2}x$ is the number half the value of the first number;

x^2 is the square of the first number.

EVALUATING EXPRESSIONS

Since we are using letters to denote numbers, we carry out the operations in the same order as in arithmetic. If we want a particular operation to be carried out when there might otherwise be ambiguity, we use brackets, so that if $x = 5$, then $(x+3) = 8$ and $x-1 = 4$ and:

$$x(x+3) = 5 \times 8 = 40$$
$$5(x-1) = 5 \times 4 = 20$$

We need to take special care where we are subtracting negative numbers.

Examples When $x = 4$, $y = -3$ and $z = -2$:

1 $x(y+5) \quad = 4(-3+5) = 4 \times 2 = 8$

2 $(x-3)(y-1) = (4-3)(-3-1)$
$\qquad\qquad\quad = 1(-4)$
$\qquad\qquad\quad = -4$

3 $x^2-2y^2-3z = \ 4^2-2(-3)^2-3(-2)$
$\qquad\qquad\qquad = 16-2(9)+6$
$\qquad\qquad\qquad = 16-18+6$
$\qquad\qquad\qquad = \ 4$

EXAMINATION QUESTIONS 11A

1 If x denotes a certain number, write down:

(a) the number 5 greater than x;
(b) the number 3 less than x;
(c) the number that is 3 times x;
(d) the number greater by 1 than twice x;
(e) the number 1 less than the square of x.

2 If the length of a rectangle is a cm and the breadth b cm, write down:

(a) the sum of the length and breadth of the rectangle;
(b) the sum of twice the length and three times the breadth;
(c) the product of the length and the breadth;
(d) the sum of the squares of the length and of the breadth;
(e) the perimeter of a rectangle whose length is 3 cm more than that of the first rectangle and whose breadth is 2 cm less.

3 Given that $a = 4$, $b = -3$, $c = -1$ and $d = 0$, evaluate:

(a) b^2
(b) $2a^2$
(c) $(3a)^2$
(d) $(a-b)^2$
(e) a^2-b^2
(f) $(a-b-c)^2$
(g) $ab-cd$

(h) $2d(a-b-2c)$
(i) a^2b
(j) a^2b
(k) $(ab)^2$
(l) $abcd$

COMMON OR 'SHOUTING' FACTOR

Two or more terms may have a factor in common, e.g.

$$xy+xz = x(y+z)$$
$$3a+12b = 3(a+4b)$$
$$6ab+15bc = 3b(2a+5c)$$
$$x^2y+xy^2+xyz = xy(x+y+z)$$

Specimen question Factorize:

$$12x^2y-9x^3+3x^2$$

Answer Notice first that each coefficient contains a factor 3, so that:

$$12x^2y-9x^3+3x^2 = 3(4x^2y-3x^3+x^2)$$

The terms inside the bracket have highest common factor x^2 (notice x^2, not just x), so that:

$$12x^2y-9x^3+3x^2 = 3x^2(4y-3x+1)$$

EXAMINATION QUESTIONS 11B

Factorize:

1 $4x-6xy$
2 $4h^2-6h$
3 $4y-12y^2$
4 x^2+3x^3
5 x^2+x^5
6 x^2+x^6
7 $2a^2+6a^3-4a^2b$
8 $3x^2y+3x^2$
9 $a^4+a^3+a^2$
10 $4x^2+8x^3+12x^4+16x^5$

DIFFERENCE OF TWO SQUARES

Since:

$$(x-y)(x+y) = x^2-y^2$$

by multiplication, we can deduce that:

$$x^2 - y^2 = (x-y)(x+y)$$

so that every expression that is the difference of two squares can be factorized, e.g.

$$a^2 - b^2 = (a-b)(a+b)$$

We may need to write one (or both) terms as a perfect square, e.g.

$$\begin{aligned} 4x^2 - y^2 &= (2x)^2 - y^2 \\ &= (2x-y)(2x+y) \end{aligned}$$

and:

$$\begin{aligned} 4x^2 - 9y^2 &= (2x)^2 - (3y)^2 \\ &= (2x-3y)(2x+3y) \end{aligned}$$

or we may need to find a common factor first, e.g.

$$\begin{aligned} x^2y - yz^2 &= y(x^2 - z^2) \\ &= y(x-z)(x+z) \end{aligned}$$

and with the occasional harder factor, the brackets may not even consist only of one term, e.g.

$$\begin{aligned} x^2 - (y-z)^2 &= \{x-(y-z)\}\{x+(y-z)\} \\ &= \{x-y+z\}\{x+y-z\} \end{aligned}$$

Examples

1   $\begin{aligned}[t] 2x^2 - 18y^2 &= 2(x^2 - 9y^2) \\ &= 2(x^2 - (3y)^2) \\ &= 2(x-3y)(x+3y) \end{aligned}$

2   $\begin{aligned}[t] \pi R^2 h - \pi r^2 h &= \pi h(R^2 - r^2) \\ &= \pi h(R-r)(R+r) \end{aligned}$

3   $\begin{aligned}[t] 1 - 16z^2 &= 1 - (4z)^2 \\ &= (1-4z)(1+4z) \end{aligned}$

EXAMINATION QUESTIONS 11C

1   $x^2 - y^2$
2   $p^2 - 49q^2$
3   $25a^2 - 9b^2$
4   $2s^2 - 18t^2$
5   $4 - 36x^2$
6   $7y - 63y^3$
7   $a^2b - c^2b$
8   $x^4 - 1$
9   $a^2 - (b-c)^2$
10   $\pi(x-y)^2 - \pi z^2$

Simplify without using tables or calculators:

11   $5.11^2 - 4.89^2$
12   $5.1^2 - 4.9^2$

13    $1001^2 - 999^2$

14    $3.14 \times 5.77 + 3.14 \times 4.23$

TRINOMIALS

Multiplying, we see that

$$(x+3)(x+4) = x(x+4)+3(x+4)$$
$$= x^2+4x+3x+12$$
$$= x^2+7x+12$$

12 is the product of $+3$ and $+4$, 7 is the sum of $+3$ and $+4$.

If we need to factorize $x^2+9x+20$, we have to find two numbers whose product is 20 and whose sum is 9. We may find $+4$ and $+5$, by trial and error. When the coefficient of x^2 is 1, trial and error is usually the simplest method.

EXAMINATION QUESTIONS 11D

Factorize:

1   x^2+7x+6
2   x^2-5x+6
3   y^2-y-6
4   z^2-5z-6
5   $x^2-4x-12$
6   $4x^2-3x-1$
7   $3x^2-x-2$
8   $3y^2-7y-6$
9   $5+6y+y^2$
10   $4x^2-2x-30$

Specimen question Factorize:

$$x^2+7x+10$$

Answer Look for two numbers whose product is 10 and whose sum is 7. Always start by finding the pairs of factors of the product. The factors of 10 are $+1$ and $+10$, $+2$ and $+5$, -1 and -10, -2 and -5. The pair whose sum is 7 is $+2$ and $+5$, so that:

$$x^2+7x+10 = (x+2)(x+5)$$

Specimen question Factorize:

$$x^2-3x-10$$

Answer Now we require two numbers whose product is -10 and whose sum is -3. Possible pairs of factors are -1 and $+10$, -2 and $+5$, -5 and $+2$, -10 and $+1$. The pair whose sum is -3 is $+2$ and -5, so that:

$$x^2-3x-10 = (x+2)(x-5)$$

When the constant term is 1, we can proceed to find numbers whose product is the coefficient of x^2, and whose sum is the coefficient of x.

Specimen question Factorize:

$$8x^2+6x+1$$

Answer The factors of 8 are 1 and 8, 2 and 4, -1 and -8, and -2 and -4. The pair whose sum is 6 is $+2$ and $+4$, so that:

$$8x^2+6x+1 = (4x+1)(2x+1)$$

When neither the coefficient of x^2 nor the constant term is 1, trial and error is sometimes shortened by the following method.

Specimen question Factorize:

$$6x^2+11x-10$$

Answer Try pairs of factors of 6 and of -10, setting out the working as below:

$$
\begin{array}{ccc}
\begin{vmatrix} 6 & 5 \\ 1 & -2 \end{vmatrix} & \begin{vmatrix} 3 & 5 \\ 2 & -2 \end{vmatrix} & \begin{vmatrix} 3 & -2 \\ 2 & 5 \end{vmatrix} \\[4pt]
-12+5=-7 & -6+10=4 & 15-4=11
\end{array}
$$

Cross-multiply the numbers and add the products; look for an arrangement in which the sum of the products is equal to the coefficient of x. The third arrangement satisfies these conditions, so the factors are:

$$(3x-2)(2x+5).$$

EXAMINATION QUESTIONS 11E

Factorize:
1. $a^2+2a+ax+2x$
2. $xy+4x+2y+8$
3. $x^2+2x+xy+2y$
4. $xy-xz-y^2+yz$
5. x^2-y^2+x+y
6. x^2-y^2+x-y
7. $z^2+3z+2+az+2a$
8. $y^2+7y+yx+10+5x$

GROUPING FACTORS

When an expression contains four terms, group them in pairs so that each pair has a common factor, e.g.

$$ax + ay - bx - by = a(x+y) - b(x+y)$$

$(x+y)$ is a common factor, so that:

$$a(x+y) - b(x+y) = (x+y)(a-b)$$

Always write the common factor, here $(x+y)$, first.

Specimen question Factorize:

$$4x - 4y + ay - ax$$

Answer

$$4x - 4y + ay - ax = 4(x-y) + a(y-x)$$

Remember that $(y-x) = -(x-y)$, so that:

$$4x - 4y + ay - ax = 4(x-y) - a(x-y)$$
$$= (x-y)(4-a)$$

Specimen question Factorize:

$$a^2 + 2ab + b^2 + a + b$$

Answer For hard factors like this, look for the trinomial first:

$$a^2 + 2ab + b^2 + a + b = (a+b)^2 + (a+b)$$
$$= (a+b)(a+b+1)$$

EXAMINATION QUESTIONS 11F

Factorize:
1 $a^2c - b^2c$
2 $a^2c - bc$
3 $a^2c - abc$
4 $ab + ac + b^2 + bc$
5 $4a^2 - 3a - 1$
6 $15 + 7t - 4t^2$
7 $2ax - 3ay - 2bx + 3by$
8 $18x^2 - 50y^2$
9 $x^2 + 4x + 4 + 10xy + 20y$
10 $a^3bc - abc$

ALGEBRA: EQUATIONS AND INEQUALITIES

CONTENTS

Summary   117

Constructing equations   118

Expressions   118

Travel problems   118

Examination questions 12A   119

Harder linear equations   120

Examination questions 12B   120

Inequalities   121

Examination questions 12C   122

Simultaneous equations   122

Examination questions 12D   124

Quadratic equations   124

▶ **Examination questions 12E**   125

Quadratic equations that cannot be factorized easily   125

▶ **Examination questions 12F**   126

▶ **Constructing equations**

Remember that an unknown x can only represent a number, so we can write
'Let Anne's speed be x kilometres per hour ...'
A person walking half as fast will walk at $\frac{1}{2}x$ kilometres per hour.
A person walking 2 kilometres per hour faster than Anne will walk at $(x+2)$ kilometres per hour.

▶ **Solving equations**

Carry out the same operation on both sides of the question, e.g.

If $\qquad \dfrac{x-1}{3} = \dfrac{2-3x}{4}$

multiply both sides of the equation by 12

$$\dfrac{12(x-1)}{3} = \dfrac{12(2-3x)}{4}$$

$\Rightarrow \qquad 4(x-1) = 3(2-3x)$

▶ **Solving inequalities**

Remember to multiply or divide both sides of an inequality by a positive number if possible so that the inequality is unaltered,

$$5x > 10 \Rightarrow x > 2$$

but $\qquad -5x > -10 \Rightarrow x < 2$

▶ **Simultaneous equations**

Elimination is usually easier than substitution for linear equations, e.g. to solve

$\qquad 7x+4y = 1 \qquad\qquad\qquad\qquad\qquad (1)$

and $\qquad 5x-3y = 2 \qquad\qquad\qquad\qquad\qquad (2)$

multiply (1) by 3 and (2) by 4 and add; addition is easier than subtraction, so choose the multipliers so that, if possible, the terms with different signs are eliminated.

CONSTRUCTING EQUATIONS

If we buy six buns for 15 pence each, the cost is 90 pence. If we buy x buns at q pence each, the cost is xq pence. Suppose we now buy six buns for 15 pence each and four buns at 20 pence each; the total cost is:

$$90p + 80p = 170p$$

We had to note clearly the meaning of each of these numbers to see which to add and which to multiply.

Suppose that a cake always costs 5 pence more than a bun. Then, if the cost of a bun is x pence, the cost of a cake is $(x+5)$ pence, i.e. 5 pence more, $x+5$. If we buy five buns, the cost of the buns is $5x$ pence. If we buy eight cakes the price is $8(x+5)$ pence. The total cost of these purchases is $5x+8(x+5)$ pence. (Notice that we have written pence in full and not used the abbreviation p. This can be confused with the unknowns in algebra problems.) If the total cost of these purchases is 235 pence, then we have the equation:

$$5x+8(x+5) = 235$$

EXPRESSIONS

We found that the total cost of the purchases was $5x+8(x+5)$ pence. This is an **expression**, which can be simplified but not solved. Here:

$$5x+8(x+5) = 13x+40$$

a simpler form for the total cost of the purchase.

TRAVEL PROBLEMS

Many problems that occur are concerned with travelling. If in doubt about the relation of distance, speed and time, always make up simple numerical questions.

Specimen question A man walks for 3 hours at x km/h and then cycles for 2 hours at $(x+5)$ km/h. How far has he travelled?

Answer If he walks for 3 hours at 6 km/h, he will travel 18 km, so if he walks for 3 hours at x km/h, he travels $3x$ km. Similarly, cycling at $(x+5)$ km/h for 2 hours, he travels $2(x+5)$ km. Thus the total distance he travels is:

$$3x+2(x+5) = 5x+10 \text{ km}$$

If we know the numerical value of the expression, as when the food cost 235 pence, we can solve the resulting equation.

When solving equations, always think what algebraic operation, like adding, subtracting, multiplying or dividing, we are doing, and make sure that we carry out the same operation on both sides of the equation. It often helps to write down what we are doing at each stage.

Specimen question A certain hotel charges £x a day for an adult and £5 less a day for a child. A family of two adults and three children stay there for 6 days and the bill is £510. How much does the hotel charge per day for an adult?

Answer Since the daily charge for a child is £5 less than the charge for an adult, the charge for a child is £$(x-5)$. The daily charge for the two adults is £$2x$, so their bill for 6 days is £$12x$. The daily charge for the three children is £$3(x-5)$, so their bill for 6 days is £$18(x-5)$.

Since the total bill is £510:
$$12x+18(x-5) = 510$$
i.e.
$$12x+18x-90 = 510$$
$$30x-90 = 510$$

Adding 90 to both sides:
$$30x = 600$$
Dividing both sides by 30:
$$x = 20$$
The daily charge for an adult is £20.

EXAMINATION QUESTIONS 12A

1 A pencil costs 2 pence more than a biro. A man buys 10 biros at x pence each, and 12 pencils. He spends £1.78 on these items. Form an equation and solve it to find the cost of a biro.

2 Railway excursion tickets for a certain journey cost £5 for an adult and £3 for a child. A party of football supporters contains five times as many adults as children; their tickets cost a total of £252.
   (*a*)   If there are x children in the party, how many adults are there?
   (*b*)   Form an equation and solve it to find x.

3 Tickets for a school concert cost either 30p or 50p each. One hundred more of the cheaper tickets were sold than the dearer. If x was the number of 50p tickets sold, write down an expression for the total receipts, in pence, from the concert. If the total receipts were £74, form an equation in x and solve it to find how many of each price of tickets were sold.

4 A girl rides x km at 10 km/h, then walks half as far at 3 km/h. If the whole journey takes 4 hours, form an equation and solve it to find how far she rides.

5 A motorist drives x km at 80 km/h then $(x+10)$ km in 4 hours. His average speed for the whole of the journey was 70 km/h. Find the length of the whole journey.

HARDER LINEAR EQUATIONS

Equations in which the only unknown is x^1 (written just x, of course) are called **linear** equations. The equations in the examination questions above were fairly easy. The principle, carrying out the same operation to both sides of the equation, holds for all equations, however difficult they may be.

Specimen question Solve for x:

$$\frac{x+1}{3} - \frac{x-2}{4} = 0$$

Answer
Points to watch.

1 The minus sign in front of the second term applies to every term obtained from that fraction.
2 Do not forget when we multiply the right-hand side (RHS) by 12, that $12 \times 0 = 0$. Even when the RHS is not zero, it is easy to forget to multiply it by the same term as the LHS.

Multiply both sides of the equation by the LCM of the denominators, i.e. 12:

$$\frac{12(x+1)}{3} - \frac{12(x-2)}{4} = 0$$

i.e.

$$4(x+1) - 3(x-2) = 0$$
$$4x+4 - 3x+6 = 0$$
$$x+10 = 0$$

Subtracting 10 from both sides:

$$x = -10$$

Check this solution by seeing if it satisfies the original equation:

$$\frac{-10+1}{3} - \frac{-10-2}{4} = -3+3 = 0$$

as expected.

EXAMINATION QUESTIONS 12B

Solve for x.

1   $5x = 4$
2   $5x-3 = 4$
3   $\dfrac{x}{3} - \dfrac{x-1}{2} = 0$
4   $\dfrac{x}{3} - \dfrac{x-1}{2} = 1$
5   $\dfrac{x}{3} - 2(x-3) = 0$

6 $\frac{x}{3} - 2(x-3) = 1$

7 $\frac{x}{3} - \frac{3-x}{2} = x$

8 $\frac{x}{4} - \frac{3-x}{8} = 3$

9 If $ax = 4$ has a solution $x = \frac{1}{2}$, find the value of a.

10 If $ax+b = 1$ has a solution $x = 2$, and b is known to be -1, find a.

INEQUALITIES

Linear inequalities are solved in the same way as linear equations, except that we have to take care that, whenever possible, we multiply or divide by positive numbers. For, although if $x > 2$, then $2x > 4$, it is also true that $-x < -2$. To verify this, $x=3$ is one value that satisfies the original inequality, but we see that $-x = -3$, which is less than -2.

Specimen question Find the range of values of x if $4x-3 < 5$.

Answer Notice that for an inequality we usually have a range of values of x, not just one value. If:

$$4x-3 < 5$$

adding 3 to both sides:

$$4x < 8$$

dividing both sides by 4:

$$x < 2$$

Specimen question Find the range of values of x if $3-4x < 5$.

Answer If:

$$3-4x < 5$$

subtracting 3 from both sides:

$$-4x < 2$$

We can now divide both sides by -4, if we remember to change the inequality:

$$x > -\tfrac{1}{2}$$

But it may be wiser to add $4x$ to both sides:

$$0 < 2+4x$$

then subtract 2 from both sides:

$$-2 < 4x$$

finally divide both sides by $+4$:

$$-\tfrac{1}{2} < x$$

Check An easy value of x which satisfies $x > -\tfrac{1}{2}$ is $x = 0$. Substituting this in the original inequality:

$$3-4(0) = 3$$

which is less than 5.

EXAMINATION QUESTIONS 12C

Find the range of values of x satisfying the following inequalities.

1   $3x-4 < 2$
2   $3x+4 < 2$
3   $4-3x < 2$
4   $4-3x < -2$
5   $2x-3(x-1) < 10$
6   $2x-3(x-1) < 5$
7   $\dfrac{x}{2} - \dfrac{2(x-1)}{3} < 1$
8   $\dfrac{x}{2} - \dfrac{2(x-1)}{3} < 0$

Form inequalities and solve them to find the range of values of x satisfying the following sets of data.

9   A boy scored $x\%$ in the first of two exams, and 8% more in the second exam, each paper being marked out of 100. His average mark was over 60%.

10 A boy bought x 10-pence stamps, and $(x+5)$ 7-pence stamps. He spent less than £5.

SIMULTANEOUS EQUATIONS

Sometimes it is easier to have two unknowns when trying to form equations from given information and to try to obtain two equations. The equations may be of the type in this example.

Specimen question Solve for x and y:

$$3x+4y = 1 \qquad\qquad (1)$$
$$2x-3y = 2 \qquad\qquad (2)$$

Answer Multiply (1) by 3:

$$9x+12y = 3 \qquad\qquad (3)$$

Multiply (2) by 4:

$$8x-12y = 8 \qquad\qquad (4)$$

Add (3) and (4) so that the terms containing y vanish:

$$17x = 11$$

$$x = \frac{11}{17}$$

Substitute in (1):

$$3\left(\frac{11}{17}\right) + 4y = 1$$

$$4y = 1 - \frac{33}{17}$$

$$= -\frac{16}{17}$$

$$y = \frac{-4}{17}$$

Check in (2):

$$2\left(\frac{11}{17}\right) - 3\left(\frac{-4}{17}\right) = \frac{22}{17} + \frac{12}{17} = 2$$

NB

1 As addition is slightly easier than subtraction, multiply the equations by suitable numbers so that the coefficients of y are equal and opposite, here 12 and -12.

2 Substitute in the equation in which the coefficient of y is positive, here equation (1).

Specimen question The sum of the ages of a father and his daughter is 43 years. Four years ago, the father was six times as old as his daughter. Find their present ages.

Answer Let the father's present age be x years and the daughter's present age be y years. Then:

$$x + y = 43$$

Four years ago, the father's age was $(x-4)$ years, and the daughter's age was $(y-4)$ years, so that:

$$x - 4 = 6(y-4)$$

i.e.

$$x - 4 = 6y - 24$$
$$x - 6y = -20$$

The equations to solve are:

$$x + y = 43 \qquad\qquad\qquad (1)$$
$$x - 6y = -20 \qquad\qquad\quad (2)$$

Subtract (2) from (1), taking care with the negative terms:

$$7y = 63$$

$$\therefore \quad y = 9$$

Substituting in (1):

$$x = 34$$

so the father's present age is 34 years, and his daughter's age is 9 years.

EXAMINATION QUESTIONS 12D

1. Solve the simultaneous equations $5x+3y = 7$
$$x-2y = 1$$

2. Solve the simultaneous equations $5x+3y = 7$
$$y-2x = 1$$

3. By factorizing the second equation, solve for x and y:

$$x-2y = 3$$
$$x^2-4y^2 = 18$$

4. The equation of a straight line can be written in the form $y = ax+b$. Find the equation of the straight line that passes through the points $(1, -1)$ and $(2, 2)$.

5. At a concert the prices of the seats were £2 and £4; programmes were 50p each. Half of those buying £4 seats bought programmes, but only one-fifth of those in £2 seats did so. The receipts from the sale of seats were £560; from the sale of programmes were £32. How many of each price of seats were sold?

QUADRATIC EQUATIONS

If the product of two numbers is zero, then one or other (or both) of those numbers must be zero. So if:

$$(x-2)(x-3) = 0$$

either $x-2 = 0$ or $x-3 = 0$. (Both cannot be equal to zero, as x cannot be equal to 2 and 3 at the same time.) If $x-2 = 0$, then $x = 2$; if $x-3 = 0$, then $x = 3$, so if:

$$(x-2)(x-3) = 0, x = 2, \text{ or } x = 3$$

To solve quadratic equations, first see if we can factorize them; if so, we can proceed as above.

Specimen question Solve for x:

$$x^2-7x+6 = 0$$

Answer If:

$$x^2-7x+6 = 0$$

$$(x-1)(x-6) = 0$$
$\therefore$ either $x-1 = 0$ or $x-6 = 0$
$\therefore$ $x = 1$ or 6

Specimen question Solve for x:

$$x^2-4x = 0$$

NB The factors of this appear to be slightly different from those above. As there is no constant term, x is a common factor.

Answer If:

$$x^2-4x = 0$$
$$x(x-4) = 0$$
$\therefore$ either $x = 0$ or $x-4 = 0$
$\therefore$ $x = 0$ or $x = 4$

EXAMINATION QUESTIONS 12E

Factorize and so solve the following quadratic equations.

1   $x^2-5x-6 = 0$
2   $x^2-7x+10 = 0$
3   $x^2+5x+6 = 0$
4   $x^2+5x = 0$
5   $3x^2+2x = 0$
6   $3x^2+2x-1 = 0$

QUADRATIC EQUATIONS THAT CANNOT BE FACTORIZED EASILY

If the equations cannot be factorized easily, we have to use a formula. It can be shown that the solutions to:

$$ax^2+bx+c = 0 \qquad (1)$$

are:

$$x = \frac{-b \pm \sqrt{(b^2-4ac)}}{2a} \qquad (2)$$

so we compare any given equation with (1).

Specimen question Solve, correct to two significant figures:

$$3x^2-4x-2 = 0$$

Answer Comparing:

$$3x^2-4x-2 = 0$$

with:

$$ax^2+bx+c = 0$$

$a = 3$, $b = -4$, and $c = -2$. Substituting these values in (2):

$$x = \frac{4 \pm \sqrt{(4^2 - 4 \times 3 \times (-2))}}{6}$$

$$= \frac{4 \pm \sqrt{40}}{6}$$

$$= \frac{4 + 6.324}{6} \text{ or } \frac{4 - 6.324}{6}$$

$$= 1.7 \text{ or } -0.39, \text{ each correct to 2 sf}$$

EXAMINATION QUESTIONS 12F

Solve the following quadratic equations, correct to two decima places.

1   $2x^2 + 4x + 1 = 0$
2   $2x^2 - 4x - 1 = 0$
3   $x^2 + x - 4 = 0$
4   $6 - 3x - 2x^2 = 0$

STRAIGHT-LINE GRAPHS

CONTENTS

▶ Summary 129

▶ 'Conversion' graphs 130

▶ Travel graphs 131

▶ Gradient 132

▶ Speed–time graphs 133
Area 133

▶ Examination questions 13A 134

▶ Straight line of 'best fit' 136

▶ Examination questions 13B 137

SUMMARY

◗ **Graphs** enable us to see the relation between two quantities, e.g. the income tax payable on taxable income (Fig. 13.1(*a*)).

Fig. 13.1(*a*)

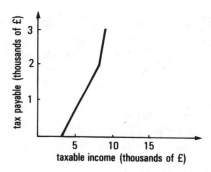

◗ Always use the **scale** given in an examination. Label the **axes** clearly, and mark where you take the readings.

◗ **Travel graphs** The position of an object (often a person) at any time can be shown on a travel graph (Fig. 13.1(*b*)). Again, use the scale given, and label the axes clearly. If the object is at rest for any period of time, that is represented by a straight line parallel to the time axis.

Fig. 13.1(*b*)

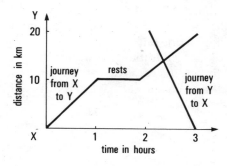

'CONVERSION' GRAPHS

Conversion graphs may be graphs enabling us to convert one currency into another, or they may be graphs that enable us to read the cost of a number of articles, or, in general, to 'convert' one variable into the corresponding value of another variable.

Always use the scale given, and label both axes clearly. Mark on your graph the points at which the readings are taken, so that, even if a mistake is made in taking the readings, the examiner can see that you are trying to take the reading at the correct place.

Specimen questions A car-hire firm A charges £10 a day for the hire of a car, plus 10p for each kilometre driven. Another car-hire firm B charges only at the rate of 15p for each kilometre driven, making no fixed charge. Draw two straight-line graphs showing the charge made by each firm for distances up to 400 km. Read from your graph the distance driven for which the two firms make the same hire charge.

Answer We shall be able to take readings easily if we use a scale of 4 cm to 100 km on the x-axis, representing the distance driven, and 2 cm to £10 on the y-axis, the cost axis. To find the charge of firm A, if their car is driven 0 km the charge is £10, so their straight line starts at (0,10); if the car is driven 200 km the charge is:

$$£(10 + \frac{10}{100} \times 200) = £30$$

If the car is driven 400 km, the charge is £50. Their hire charges are represented by the line AP in Fig. 13.1. Firm B charges 15p a km, so that there is no charge if the car is driven 0 km, and the straight-line graph goes through the origin O. For 200 km, the charge is:

$$£\frac{15}{100} \times 200 = £30$$

for 400 km the charge is £60. Their hire charges are represented by the line OQ in Fig. 13.2.

The two lines AP and OQ meet at R, whose x coordinate is 200, showing that the two firms make the same hire charge if the car is driven 200 km in one day.

There are many additional readings that we can make. To find the charge for firm A if a car is driven 150 km, read the y coordinate at K, £25; to find how far the car has been driven if the charge is £35, read the x coordinate at L, 250 km.

Fig. 13.2

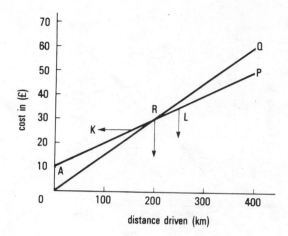

TRAVEL GRAPHS

Journeys can be represented easily on graphs. We use the x-axis to represent time and the y-axis to represent distance. Take care with readings on the time axis if your data uses hours and minutes; 30 minutes is 0.5 hours, not 0.3 hours and 15 minutes is 0.25 hours, not 0.15 hours!

Specimen question Bill sets out from Allington at 9.00 to walk to Barchester, a distance of 20 kilometres. He walks for 2 hours at 6 km/h, rests for 15 minutes then continues his journey at 5 km/h.
(*a*)   At what time does Bill reach Barchester?
(*b*)   Ben leaves Barchester at 10.00 to cycle to Allington at 15 km/h. At what time does Ben meet Bill?

Answer Bill will be 6 km from Allington at 10.00, so that we draw a straight line through the intersection of the axes and the point (10, 6) (Fig. 13.3). He walks at 6 km/h for two hours, so this line is continued up to (11, 12). He rests for 15 minutes, i.e. 0.25 h, until 11.15. Since he does not travel in this time, we draw the line parallel to the time axis. He then resumes walking at 5 km/h, so that at 12.15 he is 17 km from Allington.
    Ben leaves Barchester at 10.00, and cycles 15 km in one hour, so that at 11.00 h he is 15 km from Barchester and we can join these two points to give a straight line representing Ben's journey.
(*a*)   To find when Bill reaches Barchester, read the value of the time at point P, i.e. about 12.85 hours, which is 12 hours 51 minutes. Any value between 12.8 hours and 12.9 hours, i.e. between 12 hours 48 minutes and 12 hours 54 minutes would certainly be acceptable; we can check by calculation that the time at which they meet is 12 hours 51 minutes.

Fig. 13.3

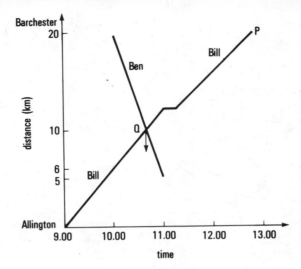

(b)   To find when Bill and Ben meet, read the time at Q. This is
between 10.6 hours and 10.7 hours, i.e. between 10 hours 36 minutes
and 10 hours 42 minutes, and our graph indicates just a little above
10.65 hours, i.e. just after 10 hours 39 minutes. By calculation we
would see that they meet at 10 hours 40 minutes.

GRADIENT

In the specimen question above, Bill walked at 6 km/h at first. In
1 hour he travelled 6 km, in 2 hours 12 km, and so on. The gradient of
the straight line representing his journey for the first 2 hours is 6 (Fig.
13.4); the gradient of the straight line representing the last stage of his
journey is 5. Ben travelled *towards* Allington, so his distance from
Allington decreases, and his gradient is negative, −15.

Fig. 13.4

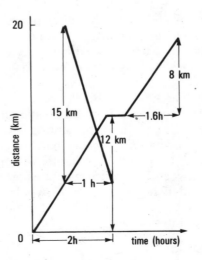

The gradient of a straight line is

$$\frac{\text{the increase in the } y \text{ coordinate}}{\text{the corresponding increase in the } x \text{ coordinate}}$$

SPEED–TIME GRAPHS

In a speed–time graph, the gradient represents the acceleration, for if the speed increases uniformly by, say, 10 m/s in 5 seconds, that is an acceleration of 2 m/s².

AREA

If we represent speed against time, a person travelling at a constant speed of 4 km/h for 3 hours will be represented by a straight line PQRS in Fig. 13.5. In 1 hour he will travel 4 km, represented by the area between PQ and the x-axis; in 2 hours he will travel 8 km, represented by the area between PQR and the x-axis; in 3 hours 12 km, represented by the area between PQRS and the x-axis. Even when the speed is varying, it is true that the distance travelled is represented by the area between the speed–time graph and the time axis.

Fig. 13.5

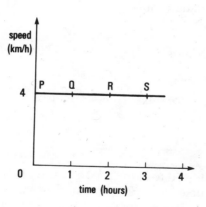

Specimen question A cyclist is initially at rest. He accelerates at a constant rate to reach a speed of 20 m/s after 10 seconds. He then travels at this constant speed for 15 seconds, finally slowing down uniformly to rest in 5 seconds. Display this information on a speed–time graph, and use your graph to find the total distance he has travelled in the 30 seconds.

Answer The graph in Fig. 13.6 shows that he accelerates up to 20 m/s in 10 seconds. Notice that the gradient of the straight line is:

$$\frac{20}{10} = 2, \text{ i.e. his acceleration is 2 m/s}^2$$

Fig. 13.6

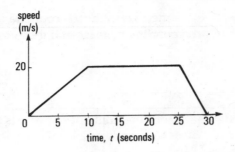

While travelling at a constant speed his acceleration is zero; while slowing down his acceleration is:

$$\frac{-20}{5} = -4\,\text{m/s}^2, \text{ i.e. his final acceleration is } -4\,\text{m/s}^2$$

The area under the speed–time graph consists of three parts. The first a triangle, area:

$$\tfrac{1}{2}\times10\times20 = 100$$

the second a rectangle, area:

$$20\times15 = 300$$

the third a triangle, area:

$$\tfrac{1}{2}\times20\times5 = 50$$

So the total area is:

$$100+300+50 = 450 \text{ units}$$

The total distance travelled is 450 metres.

EXAMINATION QUESTIONS 13A

1. A man is allowed to earn £2400 a year without paying income tax. Tax is then deducted at 40% of his salary in excess of £2400. Taking a scale of 2 cm to £1000 of income and 2 cm to £500 of tax, draw a straight-line graph to show the tax deducted on all salaries up to £8000 pa. Use this graph to find:
   (a)   the tax on a salary of £7400;
   (b)   the salary on which the tax deducted was £1000.

2. A slow train leaves Omnium for London at 9.00 h travelling at a constant 100 km/h, and a fast train leaves at 10.00 h travelling at a constant 150 km/h. If Omnium is more than 400 km from London find at what time the fast train passes the slow train.
   Why was it necessary to be told that Omnium is more than 400 km from London?

3. On a certain day the exchange value of £1 in dollars was $1.40. Draw a conversion graph on the grid in Fig. 13.7. Use your graph to find:

(a)   how many dollars can be bought for £8;

(b)   how many pounds it will cost to buy $12.

[NEA specimen question]

Fig. 13.7

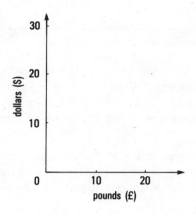

4   A particle is moving with an initial speed of 4 m/s. In the next 4 seconds its speed increases uniformly to 10 m/s, then the speed decreases uniformly until the particle stops moving after a further 8 seconds.

(a)   Show this information on a speed–time graph.

(b)   Find:

(i) the acceleration in the last 8 seconds of motion;

(ii) the total distance travelled by the particle.

[LEAG specimen question]

5   The graph in Fig. 13.8 shows Jane's journey from home to school. She walked from home to a bus stop, waited, then caught the bus to school.

Fig. 13.8

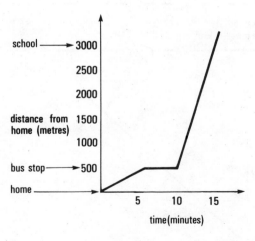

(a)   How long did it take her to walk to the bus stop?

(b)   How long did she wait at the bus stop?

(c)   How far from home was she after 13 minutes?
(d)   How far is it from the bus stop to school?

[*MEG specimen question*]

STRAIGHT LINE OF 'BEST FIT'

Sometimes there may not be an exact linear relationship between two variables, but one subject to a little variation or error. For example, although we may think that our car travels about 20 km to a litre of petrol, it is unlikely that on every journey the distance travelled on 1 litre of petrol is the same. If the distance was the same, say 20 km per litre, then:

a journey of 200 km would require 10 litres;
a journey of 140 km would require 7 litres;
a journey of 80 km would require 4 litres.

If we plot the points (10, 200), (7, 140) and (4, 80), we find that they lie on a straight line through the origin.

We can still find some useful information if we plot points corresponding to the distance travelled and then draw the straight line through the origin that is the 'best fit'. We judge 'best fit' by eye, and there must be quite a large variation permitted.

Specimen question During tests on a car the petrol consumption on certain journeys was measured and recorded as in Table 13.1. Plot points corresponding to these values and draw by eye a straight line of best fit. Use this straight line to estimate the distance travelled on a litre of petrol and the petrol likely to be required to travel 100 km.

Table 13.1

| Petrol used (litres) | 5 | 8 | 12 | 9.5 | 9 | 11 |
| Distance travelled (km) | 85 | 120 | 200 | 160 | 144 | 180 |

Fig. 13.9

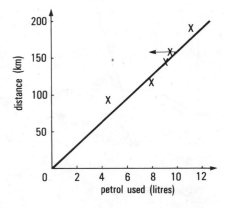

Answer We can plot the points as in Fig. 13.9 and draw by eye the straight line of best fit through the origin by placing our ruler 'on' the origin and rotating it slowly to decide which line has the 'best fit'. One possible line is given in Fig. 13.9. Using the line given, we see that the car travels 160 km on 10 litres of petrol, i.e. 16 km per litre, and that the car requires about 6.2 litres to travel 100 km.

EXAMINATION QUESTIONS 13B

1 Table 13.2 shows the prices of some paperback novels and the number of pages in them.

Table 13.2

Price	85p	£1.00	95p	£1.25	£1.50	£1.65	95p	£1.00	£1.25	65p	75p
Pages	224	254	170	236	330	380	210	190	320	136	150

On graph paper construct a scatter diagram for this information. Use scales of 2 cm to represent 50 pages and 2 cm to represent 20p.
(a)   Draw a line of best fit.
(b)   Use your line to estimate the cost of a book with 300 pages.

[*NEA specimen question*]

2 In this question state any assumptions you make.
   Jason is arrested for drunken driving at 10.30 pm on Saturday. At the police station his alcohol level is taken every hour (it is measured in milligrams per 100 millilitres of blood). A record of the measurements is kept (Table 13.3).

Table 13.3

Time after arrest (hours)	1	2	3	4	5
Level (milligrams)	160	152	139	131	120

(a)   Plot these results on a graph.
(b)   What would you expect Jason's alcohol level to be 7 hours after his arrest?
(c)   By considering a line of best fit, find a formula connecting Jason's alcohol level and the time since his arrest.
   He is released from the police station when he has a level below 80. Predictions are liable to 12% error.
(d)   What time can Jason expect to leave the police station?

[*SEG specimen question*]

GRAPHS

CONTENTS

▶ **Summary** 141

▶ **Straight-line graphs** 142

▶ **Examination questions 14A** 144

▶ **Other graphs** 144

▶ **Solution of equations** 146

▶ **Examination questions 14B** 148

▶ **Gradient of a curve** 150

▶ **Area under a curve** 151
Speed-time graph   151

▶ **Examination questions 14C** 151

SUMMARY

⬧ **Equations of the form:**

$$y = mx + c \quad \text{or} \quad ax + by = c$$

are represented by **straight-line graphs**; it is sufficient to plot three points to draw these graphs (see Figs. 14.1 and 14.2).

Fig. 14.1

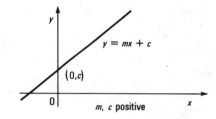

Fig. 14.2

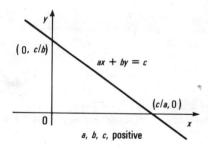

⬧ **Quadratic graphs** The graph of:

$$y = (x-a)(x+b), \ a \text{ and } b \text{ positive}$$

meets the x-axis at $x = -b$ and $x = a$ (see Fig. 14.3). To solve the equation:

$$(x-a)(x+b) = c$$

draw the straight line graph $y = c$, and read the values of x at the points of intersection P and Q.

⬧ The region *not* shaded in Fig. 14.4 is described by the **inequalities** $x>0$, $y>0$, $y>x^3-1$, and $y<x+1$.

Fig. 14.3

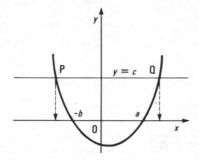

Fig. 14.4

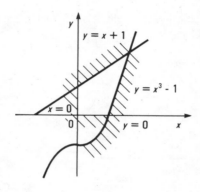

STRAIGHT-LINE GRAPHS

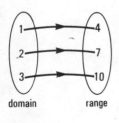

domain   range

Fig. 14.5

A function associates any one element in the domain with one and only one element in the range. Thus the function:

$$f:x \mapsto 3x+1$$

maps 1 into 4, 2 into 7, and 3 into 10 (Fig. 14.5). Since it consists only of multiples of x and constants, it is called a **linear** function of x, and may be written:

$$f(x) = 3x+1 \text{ or } y = 3x+1$$

When we plot the values of y against corresponding values of x, a straight line can be drawn through those points.

To draw the graph of a linear function, it is quite sufficient to plot three points (as in Fig. 14.6) and draw the straight line through those points. The points can be found taking any easy values of x, not too close, or can be the points at which the straight line crosses the axes, with a third point to check. Thus we can draw the graph of:

$$2x+3y = 6$$

as: $x = 0$, $y = 2$; $y = 0$, $x = 3$; and $x = 1$, $y = 1\frac{1}{3}$, so we can plot these three points.

Fig. 14.6

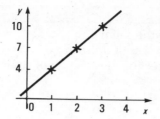

Two straight lines in general meet in a single point, and the coordinates of that point will be the solution of the simultaneous equations describing the straight lines.

Specimen question Draw the graphs of $y = x+1$ and $y = 6-x$. Read from the graphs the coordinates of the point of intersection of these straight lines.

Answer Make a table for values for each graph (Table 14.1).

Table 14.1

x	0	2	4
$x+1$	1	3	5
$6-x$	6	4	2

Generally we are given the range of values to consider, and the scales to use. Here we chose easy positive values of x to reduce the chance of arithmetic error. We might have had to take, say, $x = -2$, if the values obtained for y had not fitted on the axes.

Fig. 14.7

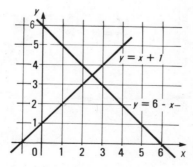

Plot the points and draw the straight lines through them (Fig. 14.7). They can be seen to intersect at $(2\frac{1}{2}, 3\frac{1}{2})$. Thus the solution of the simultaneous equations $y = x+1$ and $y = 6-x$ is $x = 2\frac{1}{2}$, $y = 3\frac{1}{2}$.

Draw the graphs of the following straight lines, for values of x from -4 to 4. Take 2 cm to 1 unit on each axis. Write down the coordinates of the point of intersection of each pair of straight lines.

1 $y = \frac{1}{2}x+1$, $y = 2-x$
2 $y = x+2$, $y = 3-x$
3 $y = 2x-1$, $y = 2-2x$
4 $y = \frac{1}{2}x-1$, $y = -x$

OTHER GRAPHS

Some of the simplest of the other graphs met at this level are the quadratic function:

$$y = x^2$$

which gives a parabola (Fig. 14.8), and the function:

$$y = \frac{1}{x}$$

which is a rectangular hyperbola (Fig. 14.9).

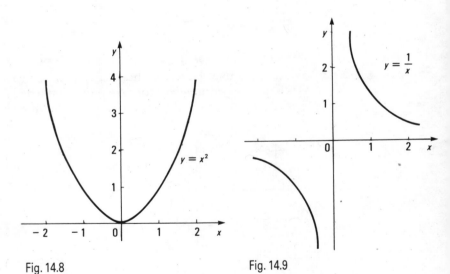

Fig. 14.8   Fig. 14.9

Many equations can be solved using only those graphs and a straight-line graph, but we may need to draw the graphs of other functions with more terms, such as:

$$y = ax^2+bx+c$$

and

$$y - a = \frac{c}{x - b}$$

and we should be familiar with more general shapes so that we know what to expect, in case of error in calculating values of y.

♦ Quadratic function (Fig. 14.10), e.g.

$$y = ax^2 + bx + c$$

Fig. 14.10

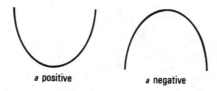

a positive   *a* negative

♦ Cubic function (Fig. 14.11), e.g.

$$y = ax^3 + bx^2 + cx + d$$

Fig. 14.11

a positive   *a* negative

(Some cubics do not have such large bends in the middle.)

♦ Hyperbola (Fig. 14.12), e.g.

$$y = 2 + \frac{3}{x}$$

Fig. 14.12

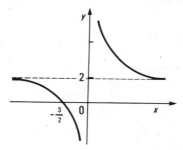

SOLUTION OF EQUATIONS

The graphs

$$y = x^2 \text{ and } y = 3-2x$$

meet where the values of y are equal for any one value of x, i.e. where:

$$x^2 = 3-2x$$

Fig. 14.13

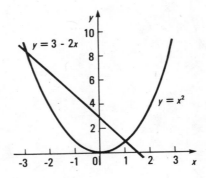

Looking at the graphs in Fig. 14.13, we see that they meet when $x = -3$ and when $x = 1$. Checking, when $x = -3$, $x^2 = 9$ and $3-2x = 9$ so that $x = -3$ satisfies the equation $x^2 = 3-2x$; in the same way, $x = 1$ satisfies that equation as well.

Specimen question Draw the graph of:

$$y = x^2 \text{ and } y = 2x+1$$

for values of x from -1 to $+3$. Read from your graph the solutions of the equation:

$$x^2-2x-1 = 0$$

Answer Since we can rearrange:

$$x^2-2x-1 = 0$$

as:

$$x^2 = 2x+1$$

we know that the points of intersection $y = x^2$ and $y = 2x+1$ will be the solutions of $x-2x-1 = 0$. We draw up a table of values for $y = x$ (Table 14.2).

Table 14.2

x	-1	-0.5	0	0.5	1	1.5	2	2.5	3
x^2	1	0.25	0	0.25	1	2.25	4	6.25	9

Since $y = 2x+1$ is straight line, three values of x will be sufficient, providing they are not too close together (Table 14.3).

Table 14.3

x	−1	1	3
$2x+1$	−1	3	7

Fig. 14.14

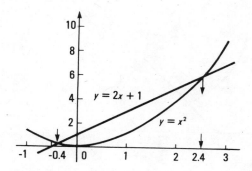

From Fig. 14.14 we see that the graphs meet where $x = -0.4$ and $x = 2.4$. Thus the solutions of:

$$x^2 - 2x - 1 = 0$$

are $x = -0.4$ or 2.4.

Specimen question Draw the graph of $y = 1/x$ for values of x from 0.5 to 2.5. Use this graph and another straight-line graph to find the positive root of the equation:

$$x^2 - x - 1 = 0$$

Answer

$$x^2 - x - 1 = 0$$

can be rearranged as:

$$x^2 - x = 1$$

i.e.

$$x - 1 = 1/x$$

so that the required root will be the point of intersection of $y = 1/x$ and $y = x - 1$ that has a positive x coordinate (Table 14.4 and Fig. 14.15).

Table 14.4

x	0.5	1	1.5	2	2.5
$1/x$	2	1	0.67	0.5	0.4

x	1	1.5	2
$x-1$	0	0.5	1

Fig. 14.15

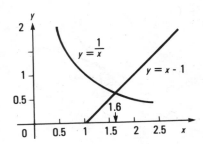

We see that the x coordinate of the point of intersection is $x = 1.6$, so that the positive root of:

$$x^2 - x - 1 = 0$$

is $x = 1.6$.

EXAMINATION QUESTIONS 14B

On paper 28 cm×20 cm, use the scale given in each question. The scale on the x-axis is given first.

1   (2 cm to 1 unit, 1 cm to 1 unit.) Draw the graph of $y = x^2$, plotting points for which $x = -3, -2, -1.5, -1, -0.5, 0, 0.5, 1, 1.5, 2, 2.5$ and 3. Use the same quadratic graph for parts (a) and (b).

(a)   Draw also the straight line $y = 3-x$ and solve the equation:

$$x^2 = 3-x$$

(b)   Draw another straight-line graph to enable you to solve:

$$x^2 = 5-2x$$

and read the solutions of this equation from your graph.

2   Repeat the graph of $y = x^2$ drawn in 1.

(a)   Draw the straight line:

$$y = \tfrac{1}{2}x+1$$

and use the graphs to solve the equation:

$$x^2 = \tfrac{1}{2}x+1$$

(b)   Draw another straight-line graph whose points of inter-section with $y = x^2$ are the roots of:

$$2x^2 - x - 4 = 0$$

Read these roots from your graph.

3 (4 cm to 1 unit on each axis.) Draw the graph of $y = 1/x$, plotting points for which $x = 0.5, 1, 1.5, 2, 2.5, 3$.

(a)   Draw the straight line $y = \frac{1}{2}x$ and read from your graphs the solution of $1/x = \frac{1}{2}x$. Why is this an approximate value for $\sqrt{2}$?

(b)   Draw another straight line through the origin to find an approximate value for $\sqrt{5}$.

4 (2 cm to 1 unit on each axis.) Draw the graph of:

$$y = \tfrac{1}{2}(x+2)(x-3)$$

for the following values of x: $-3, -2, -1, 0, \frac{1}{2}, 1, 2, 3$ and 4. Use your graph to solve the equations

(a) $\tfrac{1}{2}(x+2)(x-3) = 1$
(b) $(x+2)(x-3) = 3$

5 (5 cm to 1 unit, 1 cm to 1 unit.) Copy and complete Table 14.5 to draw the graph of:

$$y = 3x + \frac{1}{x}$$

for values of x from 0.1 to 2. Use your graph:

(a)   to find the range of values of x for which:

$$3x + \frac{1}{x} \leqslant 5$$

(b)   to solve the equation:

$$3x + \frac{1}{x} = 5 - x$$

Table 14.5

x	0.1	0.2	0.5	1	1.25	1.5	2
$3x$	0.3	0.6			3.75	4.5	
$\dfrac{1}{x}$	10.0	5.0			0.8	0.67	
$y = 3x + \dfrac{1}{x}$	10.3	5.6			4.55	5.17	

6 (2 cm to 1 unit, 2 cm to 4 units.) Draw the graph of:

$$y = x^3 - 4x$$

for values of x from -3 to $+3$ inclusive. Draw also the graph of:

$$y = x + 1.$$

(a)   Find the range of values of x for which

$$x^3 - 4x \leqslant x + 1$$

(b)   Show that the values of x at which the graphs intersect are the solutions of:

$$x^2 - 5 - \frac{1}{x} = 0$$

and draw another straight-line graph to enable you to read the solutions to:

$$x^2 - 5 - \frac{2}{x} = 0$$

(c)   Shade the region on the graph satisfying the inequalities $y \geqslant x^3 - 4x$, $y \leqslant x + 1$, and $x \geqslant 0$.

GRADIENT OF A CURVE

The gradient of a curve is the gradient of the tangent to the curve at the point P. This gradient must be drawn by eye.

Specimen question The speed of a car is given by the graph in Fig. 14.16. Draw a tangent to the graph to estimate the gradient of the curve after 8 seconds, and so estimate the acceleration after 8 seconds.

Fig. 14.16

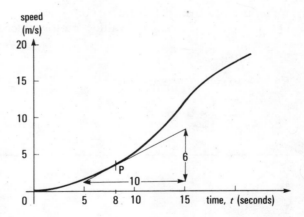

Answer On the graph we draw the tangent at point P, where $t = 8$. The gradient of the tangent is:

$$\frac{\text{increase in } y}{\text{increase in } x} = \frac{6}{10} = 0.6$$

so that the acceleration after 8 seconds is $0.6 \, \text{m/s}^2$.

AREA UNDER A CURVE

To estimate the area of the region bounded by the x-axis, a curve and, if necessary, two ordinates $x = a$ and $x = b$, we shall usually divide the region into trapezia. We know that the area of a trapezium is:

$\frac{1}{2}$ (sum of the parallel sides $\times$ perpendicular distance between them)

so that to find an approximation for the area of the region R in Fig. 14.17(a), we divide it into trapezia, as in Fig. 14.17(b). The sum of the areas in Fig. 14.17(b) is:

$$\frac{1}{2}\times5\times(0+10) + \frac{1}{2}\times5\times(10+25) + \frac{1}{2}\times5\times(25+15) + \frac{1}{2}\times5\times(15+20)$$
$$= 300$$

Fig. 14.17

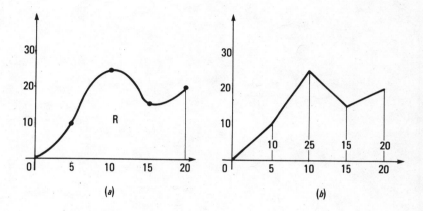

(a)   (b)

Depending on the shape of the curve, this may or may not be a good approximation to the exact area. The narrower the trapezia, the better the approximation.

SPEED–TIME GRAPH

If we have a speed–time graph, then we must remember that the area under the graph represents the distance travelled.

EXAMINATION QUESTIONS 14C

1   Taking a scale of 2 cm to 1 unit, draw the graph of:

$$y = \tfrac{1}{2}x^2$$

for values of x from 0 to 6.

(a)   Draw the tangent at the point $x = 1$ and estimate its gradient.
(b)   Draw the tangents at the points $x = 2$, 4 and 5, and estimate their gradients.

(c)   Draw a new graph of:

$$y = \tfrac{1}{2}x^2$$

for values of x from 0 to 6. Draw the line $x = 6$ to bound a region R. Estimate the area of the region R by dividing it into trapezia of width 2 units.

(d)   Find a better estimate of the area of R by dividing it into trapezia of width 1 unit.

(f)   Find an even better estimate of the area of R by dividing it into trapezia of width 0.5 unit.

INEQUALITIES: GRAPHICAL REPRESENTATION, LINEAR PROGRAMMING

CONTENTS

▶ Summary 155

▶ Graphical inequalities 156

▶ Boundaries of regions 156
Shading of regions 157

▶ Examination questions 15A 157

▶ Linear programming 158

▶ Ratios 159

▶ Examination questions 15B 160

▶ Finding the 'best solution' 161

▶ Profit lines 162

▶ Examination questions 15C 163

SUMMARY

- ◆ $<$ is less than, e.g.
  $x < 2$ reads 'x is less than 2'
- ◆ $\leq$ is less than or equal to, e.g.
  $x \leq 3$ reads 'x is less than or equal to 3'
- ◆ $>$ is greater than, e.g.
  $x > 4$ reads 'x is greater than 4'
- ◆ $\not<$ is not less than, e.g.
  $x \not< 5$ reads 'x is not less than 5'
- ◆ Shade the outer boundary of the region *not* required, e.g. unshaded region is described in Fig. 15.1 by $y < x$, and the unshaded region in Fig. 15.2 is described by:

Fig. 15.1

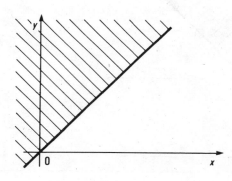

$$0 < y$$
$$0 < x < 4$$
$$x + 2y < 8$$

Fig. 15.2

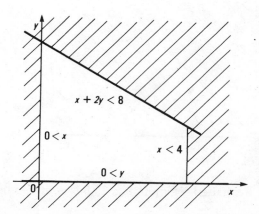

GRAPHICAL INEQUALITIES

The straight line $y = 1$ passes through all points whose y coordinate is 1. The unshaded half-plane in Fig. 15.3 contains all points whose y coordinate is less than 1, and so is described by $y < 1$. Similarly, the unshaded half-plane in Fig. 15.4 contains all the points whose y coordinate is less than their x coordinate, and so is described by $y < x$.

Fig. 15.3

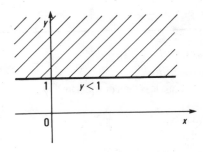

Fig. 15.4

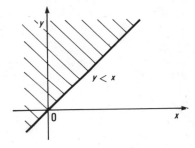

BOUNDARIES OF REGIONS

Fig. 15.5

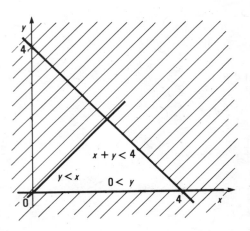

The unshaded region in Fig. 15.5 is bounded by the lines $y = 0$, $y = x$

and $x+y = 4$. All the points in the region have positive y coordinates and so are described by $y > 0$. All are such that their y coordinate is less than their x coordinate. (Take any one point, say (2,1), and verify this.) All are such that $x+y < 4$. Again, notice with the point (2,1):

$$2+1 < 4$$

If we select a point outside the region, say (3,2), we find that it does not satisfy all these conditions, e.g.

$$3+2 \not< 4$$

SHADING OF REGIONS

Since we are usually interested in the points inside a given region and we do not wish to obscure those points, we generally shade the outside boundary of the region.

Specimen question Shade the outside boundary of the region described by $x \geqslant 0$, $y \geqslant 0$ and $3x+2y \leqslant 6$.

Fig. 15.6

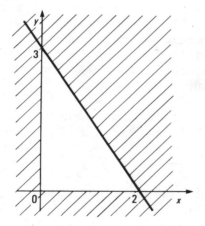

Answer To draw the straight line $3x+2y = 6$, find the points at which it meets the coordinate axes. When $x = 0$, $y = 3$; when $y = 0$, $x = 2$. A third point checks when $x = 1$, $y = 1.5$.

When trying to find which half-plane we want, the origin (0,0) is often the easiest point to use; since $3 \times 0 + 2 \times 0 < 6$, we require the half-plane containing the origin, so we shade the side of $3x+2y = 6$ *not* containing the origin (see Fig. 15.6).

EXAMINATION QUESTIONS 15A

Take a scale of 2 cm to 1 unit, and draw small sketch-graphs to illustrate each of the following.

. 1   Shade the outer boundary of the half-planes described by:

(a) $y < x$
(b) $y < x+1$
(c) $y < x+3$

2   Shade the outer boundary of the half-planes described by:

(a) $2x+y < 0$
(b) $2x+y < 2$
(c) $2x+y < 4$

3   Shade the outer boundary of the region described by the four inequalities:

$$0 < x < 4, y > 0, 2x+3y < 12$$

4   Shade the outer boundary of the region described by the four inequalities:

$$x > 1, y > 1, x+2y < 9, 2x+y < 9$$

LINEAR PROGRAMMING

In the same way that we can use graphs to solve equations, so we can use graphs, especially straight-line graphs, to describe regions in which to look for solutions of problems. This branch of mathematics has only been developed since about 1940, and has found its way into school mathematics since the 1960s. The questions set in early examinations were often rather too hard; many of them should perhaps be avoided at first. The difficulty candidates faced was in finding the algebraic inequalities to describe the situation given in words. It is most important to be able to write down the inequalities accurately.

Specimen question A taxi firm is planning to buy cars of two types, Minis and Maxis. Minis cost £3000 each, Maxis cost £5000.
(a)   If the firm buys x Minis and y Maxis, write down an inequality satisfied by x and y if the firm has £50 000 to spend on cars.
(b)   If the firm has only 15 drivers, not all of whom can work at the same time, write down another inequality satisfied by x and y.
(c)   The firm knows from past experience that they need at least five Minis; write down an inequality satisfied by x.

Answer (a) To buy x Minis at £3000 each costs £3000x; to buy y Maxis at £5000 each costs £5000y.
    Since they cannot spend more than £50 000:

$$3000x+5000y \leqslant 50\,000$$

which we can simplify to:

$$3x+5y \leqslant 50$$

(b)   The total number of cars must be less than 15, so $x+y < 15$.
(c)   Since they want at least five Minis, $x \geqslant 5$.

Points to note In (*a*) the firm could spend all the money available, so we include:

$$3x + 5y = 50$$

whereas in (*b*) not all the drivers are available at any one time, so the inequality had only $<$, not $\leqslant$.

Fig. 15.7

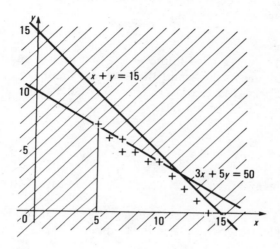

The solutions to this problem correspond to points with integer (i.e. whole number) coordinates. Some of these points are marked $+$ in the unshaded region in Fig 15.7. It is important to note what restrictions are placed on these points. Problems referring to packs of food often are such that only multiples of 5 or 6 or 10 or 12 are possible; problems referring to numbers of seats in rows usually have similar restrictions. When we have found all the possible solutions, we can then find the best.

RATIOS

The hardest inequalities to find are those based on ratio. In the specimen question above, if the firm decided that the number of Minis must be at least twice the number of Maxis, then:

$$x \geqslant 2y$$

If it decided that the ratio of Minis to Maxis must be at least 3:2, then $x{:}y \geqslant 3{:}2$, i.e.

$$\frac{x}{y} \geqslant \frac{3}{2}, \ 2x \geqslant 3y$$

Always check by seeing whether some arithmetic values satisfy the inequality obtained.

Specimen question With the data of the previous specimen question, find the inequalities to describe the following constraints.

(a)　　The number of Minis must be at least twice the number of Maxis.

(b)　　The ratio of the number of Minis to the number of Maxis must be at least 5:4.

(c)　　The number of Minis must be at least two more than the number of Maxis.

Answer

(a)　　We have found above that this is described by $x \geqslant 2y$. If we buy eight Minis and three Maxis, there are at least twice as many Minis as Maxis and $x = 8$, $y = 3$ satisfies $x \geqslant 2y$.

(b)　　Since the ratio number of Minis: number of Maxis is at least 5:4:

$$x{:}y \geqslant 5{:}4, \frac{x}{y} \geqslant \frac{5}{4}, \text{ i.e. } 4x \geqslant 5y$$

Eleven Minis and eight Maxis would satisfy this constraint, and 44 > 40.

(c)　　This constraint is not based on ratio. The number of Minis is at least two more than the number of Maxis, gives $x \geqslant y+2$.

EXAMINATION QUESTIONS 15B

Write down inequalities to describe the following.

1　A man is planning to grow x tomato plants and y cucumber plants in his greenhouse.

(a)　　The total number of plants must not be more than 20.

(b)　　Tomatoes cost 25p each and cucumbers 75p each; he must not spend more than £8.

(c)　　There must be at least 10 tomato plants.

(d)　　There must be at least 4 cucumber plants.

(e)　　These must be at least 2 more tomato plants than there are cucumber plants.

(f)　　There must be at least twice as many tomato plants as cucumbers.

(g)　　He allows 0.8 m² of floor space for each tomato plant and 1 m² for each cucumber; he has only 15 m² of floor space available.

2　A car park is to be laid out for x cars and y lorries.

(a)　　There must be room are at least 50 cars.

(b)　　The number of lorries must not be more than 20.

(c)　　The total number of cars and lorries must not be more than 40.

(d)　　Cars are allowed 10 m² of space, lorries 20 m², and there is only 2000 m² available.

(e)　　The ratio of the number of cars to the number of lorries must be at least 3:1.

(*f*)   There must be at least 20 more cars than lorries.

FINDING THE 'BEST SOLUTION'

Since the inequalities describe a region, not just a point, we usually have several solutions, and can choose the one that is 'best'. If we have to find a profit, we shall usually want to choose the solution that gives as much profit as possible. If we have to find a cost, we shall usually want to have the solution that makes the cost as small as possible.

Specimen question At a school play, the audience is seated partly in chairs and partly on stools. If there are x chairs and y stools, write down inequalities to describe the following constraints.
(*a*)   There must be at least 100 seats available.
(*b*)   There are only 120 stools available.
(*c*)   There must be at least twice as many stools as there are chairs.
(*d*)   The school allows 1 m² of floor space for a chair and 0.6 m² for a stool; the area of the floor is 90 m².
Draw straight-line graphs representing these inequalities, and shade the outside boundary of the region in which lie the points corresponding to all possible values of x and y satisfying these conditions. If chairs must be placed in rows of 10 and stools in rows of 12, mark on the diagram all points corresponding to possible numbers of each seat.
    How many of each type of seat should be provided to make the receipts as large as possible, assuming that all seats provided will be sold, if the prices of tickets are:
(*e*)   70p for a chair and 60p for a stool;
(*f*)   50p for a chair and 30p for stool?

Answer Write down inequalities from the constraints as listed.
(*a*)   Since the total number of seats must be at least 100:

$$x+y \geqslant 100$$

(*b*)   Since there are only 120 stools available:

$$y \leqslant 120$$

(*c*)   There must be at least twice as many stools as chairs:

$$y \geqslant 2x$$

(Check: 20 chairs, 50 stools would satisfy this constraint, and $x = 20$, $y = 50$ satisfies the inequality.)
(*d*)   Since there is only 90 m² of floor space available:

$$x+0.6y \leqslant 90$$

Fig. 15.8

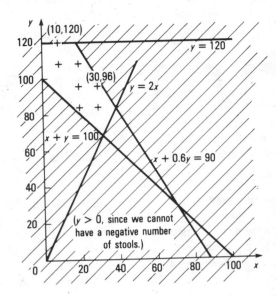

These straight lines are drawn in Fig. 15.8. Since chairs are in rows of
10 and stools in rows of 12, the only possible solutions are those in
which x is a multiple of 10 and y a multiple of 12. Points corresponding to these are marked + in Fig. 15.8.

To find the solution that gives most receipts, we shall want to
choose large values of x and y. From Fig 15.8, clearly $x = 30$, $y = 96$
looks likely to be a good possibility, and we calculate that the
receipts, at 70p a chair and 60p a stool, would be £78.60. But if we try
$x = 10$, $y = 120$ we have receipts of £79.00, a slightly better solution.

On the other hand, if the seats are priced at 50p and 30p, then
$x = 30$, $y = 96$ gives £43.80, whereas $x = 10$, $y = 120$ only yields £41
so that for these prices, the best distribution of seats is 30 chairs and
96 stools.

PROFIT LINES

Consider the last specimen question and suppose that the prices are
70p for a chair and 50p for a stool. Then if we have x chairs and
stools, the receipts are $(70x+50y)$ pence. If we provide 40 chairs and
60 stools the receipts would be £58, and the point (40, 60) is seen to l
on the straight line:

$$70x+50y = 5800$$

If we provide 60 of each, the receipts are £72, and the point (60, 6
lies on the line:

$$70x+50y = 7200$$

Clearly these receipt lines are all parallel, and the further the lines ar
from the origin, the greater the receipts (Fig. 15.9).

Draw any one receipt line:

$$70x + 50y = \text{any constant (even 0)}$$

and then draw the line parallel to this, through a point that is a possible solution.

Fig. 15.9

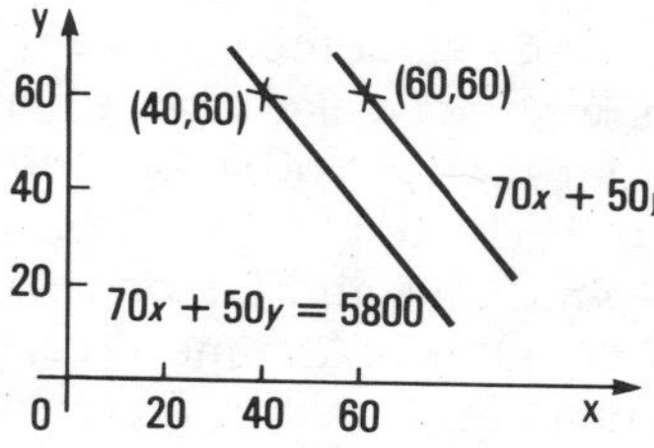

The line furthest from the origin passing through one of the points × gives the best solution. Here we see that

$$70x + 50y = 6700$$

passes through the point (10, 120), and is slightly nearer the origin than

$$70x + 50y = 6900$$

through the point (30, 96), so that, at these prices, 10 chairs and 120 stools is not quite as profitable an arrangement as 30 chairs and 96 stools. Although these lines, giving quantities that we want to make as large as possible (i.e. maximize), do not necessarily represent profits, these are usually called 'profit lines'. Quantities that we want to minimize (make as small as possible) we usually find by drawing 'cost lines', as close as possible to the origin.

Although profit lines and cost lines are very useful in solving harder problems, many find that, at this stage, trial and error of the likely solutions is usually a simpler method.

EXAMINATION QUESTIONS 15C

1   A small businessman is equipping a factory with two types of machine, X and Y. Each machine of type X needs 10 m² of floor space and each machine of type Y needs 7 m²; he has 150 m² available. Machines X cost £500 each, machines Y cost £1200 each; he has £16 000 to spend on machines.

Write down two inequalities from this data. Using the extra inequalities $x \geq 0$ and $y \geq 0$, where x and y are the number of machines he buys of each type, draw four straight-line graphs and shade the outer boundary of the region which gives all possible numbers of each type he can buy.

If the monthly profit on each machine of type X is £100, and on each machine of type Y is £80, how many of each type should he buy to make as much profit as possible?

If, however, the profit on each machine of type X is £90 and each machine of type Y is £60, how many of each should he buy to make as much profit as possible?

2   A certain village bakery produces only two types of fruit cake, round and square; the mixture in each is the same. Round cakes contain 0.75 kg of mixture and each square cake contains 1 kg of mixture; the bakery can only make 24 kg of mixture a day. From experience, they know they always want to make more square cakes than round. If they make 12p profit on a round cake, and 13p profit on a square cake, how many of each should they bake a day? If, however, the profit is 13p on a round cake and 12p on a square cake, how many of each should they bake a day? (Assume all cakes baked are sold.)

3   A schoolmaster is planning to retire and run a holiday kennel for dogs and cats. He estimates that each dog needs 10 m² of space and each cat 7 m²; he has 150 m² available. He intends to have more cats than dogs, but does not wish the ratio of the number of cats to the number of dogs to be greater than 3:2. Write down three inequalities to describe these constraints.

How many of each should he plan to have to accommodate as many animals as possible?

GEOMETRY: PARALLEL LINES, TRIANGLES, ISOMETRY, QUADRILATERALS

CONTENTS

▶ **Summary**   **167**

▶ **Parallel lines, corresponding, alternate, and adjacent angles**   **167**

▶ **Triangles**   **168**
Isoceles and equilateral   168
Areas of triangles   169

▶ **Examination questions 16A**   **169**
Congruent triangles   170

▶ **Reflection**   **171**

▶ **Rotation**   **172**

▶ **Translation**   **172**

▶ **Isometries**   **173**

Contents

▶ **Examination questions 16B**   **173**

▶ **Quadrilaterals**   **174**
Parallelogram   174
Rhombus   174
Rectangle   175
Square   175
Kite   175
Relations between quadrilaterals   175

▶ **Examination questions 16C**   **175**

SUMMARY

- A triangle with no sides equal is called a **scalene** triangle.
- A triangle with two (or more) sides equal is called an **isosceles** triangle.
- A triangle with all three sides equal is called an **equilateral** triangle.
- A quadrilateral with both pairs of opposite sides parallel is called a **parallelogram**.
- A parallelogram with two adjacent sides equal is called a **rhombus**.
- A parallelogram with one angle a right angle is called a **rectangle**.
- A rectangle with adjacent sides equal is called a **square**.
- Some properties of **parallel lines**:
  corresponding angles and **alternate** angles are equal;
  adjacent angles are supplementary.
- The sum of the angles of a triangle is two right angles.
  (Corollary: the sum of the angles of an n-sided polygon is $(2n-4)$ right angles.)
- In any right-angled triangle, the square on the hypotenuse is equal to the sum of the squares on the other two sides (Pythagoras' theorem).
- The angle subtended by an arc of a circle at the centre is double the angle subtended by that arc at any other point on the remaining part of the circumference.
  (Corollaries: angles in the same segment of a circle are equal; the opposite angles of a cyclic quadrilaterial are supplementary; the angle in a semi-circle is a right angle.)
- If two chords AB, CD of a circle intersect at a point X:

$$AX \cdot XB = CX \cdot XD$$

- Equiangular triangles have their corresponding sides proportional.

PARALLEL LINES, CORRESPONDING, ALTERNATE, AND ADJACENT ANGLES

In Fig. 16.1, AB is parallel to CD. Pairs of corresponding angles are a and c, h and b, g and e, f and d; corresponding angles are **equal**. Pairs of alternate angles are f and b, a and e; alternate angles are **equal**. Pairs of adjacent angles are a and b, f and e; adjacent angles are **supplementary**, i.e. total 180°. Simple questions, some of them in multiple choice papers, are set testing only these properties.

Fig. 16.1

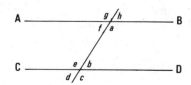

Specimen question In Fig. 16.2, PQ is parallel to TS. Which of the following statements is true?

Fig. 16.2

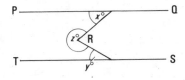

(a)	$x+y = z$
(b)	$x+y+z = 180$
(c)	$x+y+z = 270$
(d)	$x+y+z = 360$

Answer Draw the line RU through R parallel to PQ (Fig. 16.3). (This construction is often helpful.) Then angle QRU = $x°$ (alternate) and SRU = $y°$. These two angles, with angle $z°$, complete a full circle, so $x+y+z = 360$. The answer is (d).

Fig. 16.3

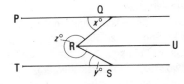

TRIANGLES

ISOSCELES AND EQUILATERAL

An isosceles triangle has a pair of sides equal in length; an equilateral triangle has three sides equal in length, so that all equilateral triangles are isosceles, a relation often tested in questions using Venn diagrams.

Specimen questions If $\mathscr{E}$ = {All triangles}, A = {All isosceles triangles}, B = {All equilateral triangles}, C = {All right-angled triangles}, draw a Venn diagram illustrating the relation between the sets. Show that all elements of the set $A \cap C$ are similar, and that:

$$B \cap C = \varnothing.$$

Answer The relation between the sets is illustrated by the Venn diagram in Fig. 16.4. Since all triangles in the set $A \cap C$ are isosceles and right-angled, the angle sizes must be 45°, 45°, 90°, so the triangles are similar. Since all equilateral triangles have all angles equal to 60°, no equilateral triangle contains a right angle:

Take a/w Fig. 16.4

Fig. 16.4

$$B \cap C = \varnothing$$

AREAS OF TRIANGLES

The area of a triangle is:

$\frac{1}{2}$ base × perpendicular height

Since the perpendicular through the vertex of an isosceles triangle bisects the base this sometimes helps in calculating the area of isosceles triangles. We can also use the formula for the area of a triangle to calculate the height of the triangle.

Specimen question In the isosceles triangle ABC, AB = AC = 17 cm and BC = 16 cm. Calculate the area of the triangle, and hence the perpendicular distance of B from AC.

Answer Draw the perpendicular bisector of BC, to meet BC in D. Then by Pythagoras' theorem, $AB^2 = AD^2 + BD^2$, i.e.

$$AD^2 = 17^2 - 8^2$$
$$= 225$$
$$AD = 15$$

so:

area of triangle ABC $= \frac{1}{2} \times 16 \times 15 = 120 \text{ cm}^2$

Regarding AC as the base, and taking the perpendicular distance of B from AC as p (Fig. 16.5):

$$\frac{1}{2} \times 17 \times p = 120,$$
$$p = \frac{240}{17},$$
$$= 14.1, \text{ to 3 sf}$$

The perpendicular distance of B from AC is about 14.1 cm.

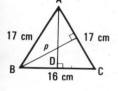

Fig. 16.5

EXAMINATION QUESTIONS 16A

Fig. 16.6

1   In Fig. 16.6, AB is parallel to PQ. Copy the following statements, and complete each, using one of the words **alternate**, **corresponding**, **supplementary**.

(a)   Angles x and a are . . .
(b)   Angles x and b are . . .
(c)   Angles x and c are . . .
(d)   Angles x and d are . . .

2   In Fig. 16.7, AB is parallel to PQ. If AX and PX are the angle bisectors, prove that $A\hat{X}P = 90°$.

Fig. 16.7

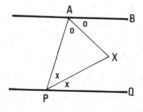

Fig. 16.8

3 One angle of an isosceles triangle is twice another angle. Find the sizes of the angles in the triangle.

4 In the triangle ABC, AB = 8 cm, BC = 9 cm, and ABC = 90°. Find the area of the triangle, and hence the perpendicular distance of B from AC.

5 In Fig. 16.8 an equilateral triangle ABC is inscribed in a square ABPQ. Calculate the angle BCP.

CONGRUENT TRIANGLES

Two triangles are congruent if one can be superimposed on to the other. We can think of this 'placing on top' being done by reflection, by rotation, or by translation, or we can show that it is possible to carry out the superposition because certain sides and angles are equal.

Thus two triangles are congruent if AB = XY, BC = YZ, and CA = ZX, as these lengths determine a triangle uniquely (Fig. 16.9). This case of congruence is denoted by **SSS** (side, side, side).

Fig. 16.9

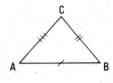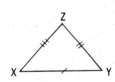

In Fig. 16.10, the triangles will be congruent if AB = XY, BC = YZ and angle ABC = angle XYZ. Again, a triangle is uniquely determined. This case of congruence is denoted **SAS** (side, included angle, side).

Fig. 16.10

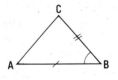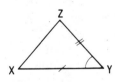

In Fig. 16.11, the triangles wil be congruent if AB = XY, angle CAB = angle ZXY, angle XYZ = angle ABC. This case is abbreviated **ASA** (angle, side, angle).

Fig. 16.11

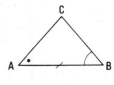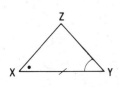

The final case of congruency is illustrated in Fig. 16.12, where the triangles have **two pairs of sides equal**, and one angle of each triangle is a **right angle**.

Fig. 16.12

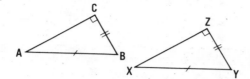

Notice (Fig. 16.13) that two triangles are *not* congruent if two pairs of sides are equal and a pair of not-included angles are equal, for two different triangles could be constructed from that data.

Fig. 16.13

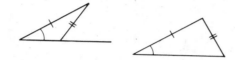

REFLECTION

Fig. 16.14

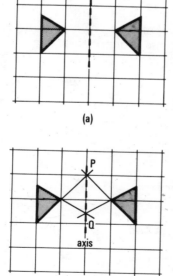

(a)

(b)

If one figure is reflected in a certain straight line to give another figure, the straight line is called the **axis of reflection**. To find the axis, take any straight line in one figure, and its image in the other figure. Produce both until they meet in a point P. Select another straight line and its image, and produce them until they meet in a point Q. Then the line PQ will be the axis of reflection (Fig. 16.14).

ROTATION

To find the centre of rotation, if P' is the image of a point P under a certain rotation, PP' must be a chord of a circle, whose centre is the centre of the rotation, so the centre of the rotation must lie on the perpendicular bisector of PP'. Similarly, if Q' is the image of a point Q, the centre lies on the perpendicular bisector of QQ' (Fig. 16.15).

Fig. 16.15

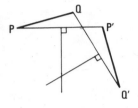

TRANSLATION

In a translation, the whole figure is moved a certain distance in a given direction. We may be given the components of the translation in two fixed directions in matrix form, e.g.

$$\begin{pmatrix} 3 \\ 1 \end{pmatrix}$$

describes the translation in Fig. 16.16.

Fig. 16.16

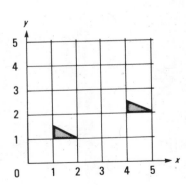

ISOMETRIES

These operations of reflection, rotation and translation are sometimes called **isometries**, because lengths are not altered. By contrast, in an **enlargement**, obviously lengths are altered.

Specimen question In Fig. 16.17, AB = AD, AC = AE and BC = DE. Prove that triangles BAE, DAC are congruent.

Fig. 16.17

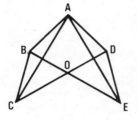

Answer In triangles ABC, ADE:

AB = AD (given)
BC = DE (given)
AC = AE (given)

∴ triangles ABC, ADE are congruent (**SSS**).
Since these triangles are congruent:

angle BAC = angle DAE

Adding angle CAE to each:

angle BAE = angle CAD

In triangles BAE, DAC,

AB = AD (given)
angle BAE = angle CAD (proved)
AE = AC (given)

Therefore triangles BAE, DAC are congruent (SAS).

Alternatively, we can show that AO is the axis of symmetry of the figure, and that triangle BAE reflects in AO to give triangle DAC.

EXAMINATION QUESTIONS 16B

1   In Fig. 16.18, ABCD is part of a regular 20-sided polygon. Prove that AC = BD by (a) using congruent triangles, (b) by finding the centre of a certain rotation.

Fig. 16.18

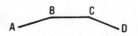

2   In an isosceles triangle ABC, X is the midpoint of AB and Y the midpoint of AC. Prove that CX = BY by (a) using congruent triangles, (b) using a certain reflection.

3   In Fig. 16.19, ABCD is a rectangle. P is the midpoint of BC, Q the midpoint of AD; AX:XB = CY:YD = 2:1. Prove, by two methods, that XP = QY.

Fig. 16.19

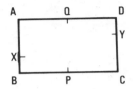

QUADRILATERALS

PARALLELOGRAM

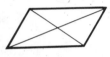

Fig. 16.20

A parallelogram (Fig. 16.20) is defined as a quadrilateral with both pairs of opposite sides parallel. From this definition we can prove:

1   both pairs of opposite sides are equal;
2   both pairs of opposite angles are equal;
3   the diagonals bisect each other.

It is a useful exercise in congruent triangles, and in the symmetry of the figure, to prove these.

NB A parallelogram has rotational symmetry about the intersection of the diagonals, and is *not* symmetrical about a diagonal, unless it is a rhombus.

RHOMBUS

A parallelogram with one pair of adjacent sides equal is called a rhombus (Fig. 16.21). It can be proved, and again is a useful exercise in congruent triangles or the symmetry of the figure, that:

1   all sides of a rhombus are equal;
2   the diagonals of a rhombus bisect each other at right angles;
3   each diagonal of a rhombus bisects the angles through which it passes.

Fig. 16.21

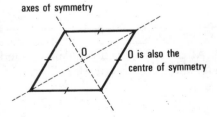

axes of symmetry

O is also the centre of symmetry

RECTANGLE

A parallelogram with one angle a right angle is called a rectangle. It can be proved that:

1 all angles of a rectangle are right angles;
2 the diagonals of a rectangle are equal.

SQUARE

A rectangle with two adjacent sides equal is called a square. A square has all the properties of the parallelogram, rhombus, and rectangle.

KITE

A quadrilateral with two pairs of adjacent sides equal is called a kite. A kite has one axis of symmetry, and its diagonals meet at right angles.

RELATIONS BETWEEN QUADRILATERALS

The relation between these types of quadrilaterals is illustrated in Fig. 16.22. If $\mathcal{E} = \{$all quadrilaterals$\}$:

Fig. 16.22

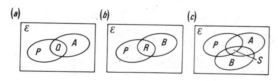

◆ in Fig. 16.22(a), $P = \{$all parallelograms$\}$, $A = \{$all quadrilaterals with at least one pair of adjacent sides equal$\}$ and $Q = \{$all rhombuses$\}$, then:

$$P \cap A = Q$$

◆ $B = \{$all quadrilaterals with at least one right angle$\}$ and $R = \{$all rectangles$\}$, then (Fig. 16.22(b)):

$$P \cap B = R$$

◆ $S = \{$all squares$\}$, then (Fig. 16.22(c)):

$$P \cap A \cap B = S$$

EXAMINATION QUESTIONS 16C

1 If $K = \{$all kites$\}$, $P = \{$all parallelograms$\}$, and $R = \{$all rhombuses$\}$, draw a Venn diagrams to illustrate the relation between the sets K, P and R.

2 If $\mathcal{E} = \{$all quadrilaterals$\}$, $P = \{$all parallelograms$\}$, $R = \{$all

rectangles}, S = {all squares}, T = {all trapezia}, V = {all rhombuses}, which of the following are true?

(a) $S \subset R$

(b) $V \subset P$

(c) $R \subset P$

(d) $P' \subset R'$

(e) $P \subset T$

(f) $T' \subset S'$

NB A trapezium is a quadrilateral with one pair of opposite sides parallel.

COMMONLY USED THEOREMS

CONTENTS

▶ **Summary** — 179

▶ **The sum of the angles in a triangle** — 180

▶ **The sum of the angles of an *n*-sided polygon** — 180

▶ **Regular polygons** — 181

▶ **Examination questions 17A** — 181

▶ **Pythagoras' theorem** — 181
Converse 182

▶ **Examination questions 17B** — 183

▶ **Circle theorems** — 183
Tangents 185
Alternate segment theorem 186
Intersecting chord theorem 186

▶ **Examination questions 17C** — 187

▶ **Similar triangles** — 188

Contents

▶ **Enlargement** **188**

▶ **Examination questions 17D** **190**

SUMMARY

- The angle sum of the angles of a triangle is 180°.
- The sum of the angles of a quadrilateral is 360°.
- The sum of the angles of a pentagon is 540°.
- The sum of the angles of a polygon with n sides is $(2n-4) \times 90°$.

- **Pythagoras' theorem**

  The square on the hypotenuse of a right-angled triangle is equal to the sum of the squares on the other two sides.

Fig. 17.1(*a*)

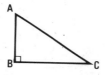

- **Circle theorems**

  The angle subtended by an arc of a circle at the centre is twice the angle subtended by that arc at a point on the circumference of the circle.

Fig. 17.1(*b*)

- **Corollaries**
1. Angles in the same segment of a circle are equal.
2. The angle in a semicircle is a right angle.

Fig. 17.1(*c*)

$x + y = 180°$

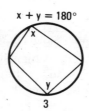

1 2 3 4

3 Opposite angles of a cyclic quadrilateral are equal.
4 The exterior angle of a cyclic quadrilateral is equal to the interior opposite angle.

◆ **Tangents**
1 A tangent to a circle is perpendicular to the radius through the point of contact.

Fig. 17.1(*d*)

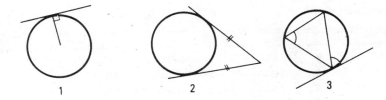

1   2   3

2 Tangents from a point are equal in length.
3 The angle between a tangent and a chord through the point of contact is equal to the angle in the alternate segment.

◆ **Intersecting chord theorem**
In Fig. 17(*e*), $AX.XB = CX.XD = XT^2$

Fig. 17.1(*e*)

 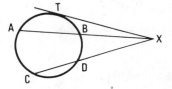

THE SUM OF THE ANGLES IN A TRIANGLE

In Fig. 17.2, by drawing the straight line through B parallel to AC, we can prove that:
◆ the exterior angle of a triangle is equal to the sum of the two interior opposite angles; and
◆ the sum of the angles of the triangle ABC is 180°.

Fig. 17.2

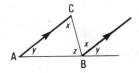

THE SUM OF THE ANGLES OF AN *n*-SIDED POLYGON

By choosing a suitable point P inside the polygon (Fig. 17.3), we can construct *n* triangles. The sum of the angles in these triangles is $2n$ right angles. But there are four right angles at the point P, so that the sum of the angles of the polygon is $(2n-4)$ right angles.

Fig. 17.3

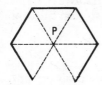

REGULAR POLYGONS

A regular polygon has all sides equal and all angles equal. Thus each angle of a regular polygon has

$$\frac{1}{n}(2n-4) \text{ degrees (Fig. 17.5)}$$

Fig. 17.4

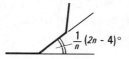

It is usually easier to calculate the exterior angle of a regular polygon, then find the interior one by subtraction from 180°.

Specimen question Find the interior angle of a regular 12-sided polygon.

Answer Since the exterior angles total 360°, each will be $\frac{1}{12}\times360°$, i.e. 30° (Fig. 17.5), so that the interior angles will be 150°.

Fig. 17.5

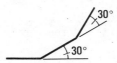

EXAMINATION QUESTIONS 17A

1   Find the size of each interior angle of a regular 15-sided polygon.
2   Each angle of a regular polygon is 162°. How many sides has the polygon?
3   Which of the following cannot possibly be an exterior angle of a regular polygon?
    (a)   12°   (b)   15°   (c)   16°   (d)   18°

PYTHAGORAS' THEOREM

▶   In a right-angled triangle, the square on the hypotenuse is equal to the sum of the squares on the other two sides.

When applying this theorem, always write down the square on the hypotenuse first, then the squares on the other two sides.

CONVERSE

It is sometimes necessary to distinguish between a theorem and its converse. The converse of Pythagoras' theorem illustrates this distinction. The converse is that if, in a triangle the square on one side is equal to the sum of the squares on the other two sides, then the angle opposite the longest side is a right angle.

This can be extended to show that if in a triangle the square on one side is greater than the sum of the squares on the other two sides, then the angle opposite the longest side is greater than a right angle. A similar result holds if the relation is 'less than'.

Specimen question In the triangle ABC (Fig. 17.6), AD = 6 cm, BD = 4 cm and DC = 9 cm. AD is perpendicular to BC. Prove that angle BAC is a right angle.

Fig. 17.6

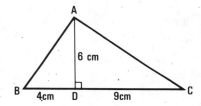

Answer Since $B\hat{D}A = 90°$:

$$AB^2 = BD^2 + DA^2 \text{ (Pythagoras' theorem)}$$
$$= 4^2 + 6^2$$
$$= 52$$

Since $A\hat{D}C = 90°$:

$$AC^2 = AD^2 + DC^2 \text{ (Pythagoras' theorem)}$$
$$= 6^2 + 9^2$$
$$= 117$$

In triangle ABC:

$$AB^2 + AC^2 = 52 + 117$$
$$= 169$$
$$= 13^2$$
$$= BC^2$$

Therefore angle BAC is a right angle (converse of Pythagoras' theorem).

1   In the triangle ABC, angle ABC = 90°, AB = 7 cm, and BC = 24 cm. Calculate the length of AC.

2   In the right-angled triangle ABC, AB = 8 cm and BC = 15 cm. Find the two possible lengths for AC.

3   In triangle ABC, AB = 11 cm, BC = 13 cm, and AC = 17 cm. Is angle ABC greater than, equal to, or less than a right angle?

4   Show that, for all values of m, any triangle whose sides are in the ratio $(m^2+1):2m:(m^2-1)$ is right-angled.

5   In the triangle ABC, angle ABC = 90°. If M is the midpoint of AC, show that $AB^2+BC^2 = 2AM^2+2BM^2$. (Hint; draw BN perpendicular to AC to meet AC at N.)

CIRCLE THEOREMS

●   A point in a plane whose distance from a fixed point in that plane is constant lies on the circumference of a **circle**.

●   The length of the circumference of a circle radius r is $2\pi r$.

●   The area enclosed by the circle is πr^2.

●   A straight line joining two points on the circumference of a circle is a **chord** of the circle.

●   A chord through the centre of a circle is called a **diameter**.

Fig. 17.7

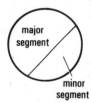

major segment

minor segment

●   A chord cuts a circle into two **segments** (Fig. 17.7).

Fig. 17.8

●   Two radii determine a **sector** of a circle (Fig. 17.8).
    If the angle between the radii is $\theta°$:

$$\text{the length of the arc is } \frac{\theta}{360} \times 2\pi r$$

$$\text{the area of the sector is } \frac{\theta}{360} \times \pi r^2$$

From the definition of the circle it follows that we have many isosceles triangles, which can be used in calculations and proofs on the circle. A circle is also symmetrical about every line through its centre.

♦ The angle which an arc of a circle subtends at the centre of a circle is twice that subtended by the arc at any other point on the circumference of the circle.

Fig. 17.9

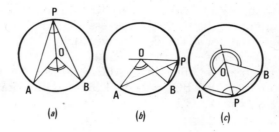

(a)   (b)   (c)

Fig. 17.9 illustrates the three possible cases. The theorem follows immediately from the definition, triangles OAP, OBP being isosceles, and the exterior angle of a triangle being equal to the sum of the two interior angles. There are several important corollaries to this theorem.

Fig. 17.10

1   Angles in the same segment of a circle are equal (Fig. 17.10).
2   The angle in a semicircle is a right angle (Fig. 17.11).
3   The opposite angles of a cyclic quadrilateral are supplementary (Fig. 17.12(a)), and hence the exterior angle of a cyclic quadrilateral is equal to the interior opposite angle (Fig. 17.12(b)).

These should be known thoroughly as they are tested regularly in those examinations in which they are part of the syllabus.

Fig. 17.11

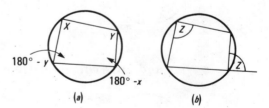

Fig. 17.12   (a)   (b)

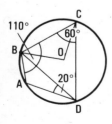

Fig. 17.13

Specimen question In Fig. 17.13, angle ABC = 110°, BCD = 60°, angle BDA = 20°. Calculate the angles ADC, BAC, ACD, BOC and CBO.

Answer

$A\hat{D}C = 180° - 110°$ (opposite angles of a cyclic quadrilateral are supplementary)

$\therefore A\hat{D}C = 70°$

Since $A\hat{D}C = 70°$:

$$B\hat{D}C = 70° - 20° \quad (B\hat{D}A = 20°, \text{ given})$$
$$= 50°$$

But:

$$B\hat{A}C = B\hat{D}C \text{ (angles in same segment)}$$
$$\therefore B\hat{A}C = 50°$$

Now:

$$B\hat{C}A = B\hat{D}A = 20° \text{ (angles in same segment)}$$
$$\therefore A\hat{C}D = B\hat{C}D - B\hat{D}A = 60° - 20°$$
$$\therefore \underline{A\hat{C}D = 40°}$$
$$\underline{B\hat{O}C = 100°} \text{ (angle subtended by an arc at the centre of a}$$
$$\text{circle is twice the angle subtended by that arc}$$
$$\text{at a point on the circumference of a circle)}$$

Since:

$$B\hat{O}C = 100°$$
$$B\hat{C}O + C\hat{B}O = 80° \text{ (angle sum of triangle)}$$
$$\therefore \underline{B\hat{C}O = 40°} \text{ CBO is an isosceles triangle, since OB = OC,}$$
$$\text{radii)}$$

Specimen question Two circles intersect at points C and D, as in Fig. 17.14. BCY and ADX are straight lines. Prove that AB is parallel to XY.

Fig. 17.14

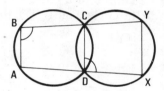

Answer In the cyclic quadrilateral ABCD, $A\hat{B}C = C\hat{D}X$ (exterior angle of a cyclic quadrilateral is equal to the interior opposite angle).

In the cyclic quadrilateral CDXY, $C\hat{D}X + X\hat{Y}C = 180°$ (opposite angles of a cyclic quadrilateral are supplementary).

$\therefore A\hat{B}C$ and $C\hat{Y}X$ are supplementary,

$\therefore$ AB is parallel to XY ($A\hat{B}C$, $C\hat{Y}X$ adjacent angles).

NB Always be perfectly clear about the reason for any statement or calculation. Do not confuse *equal* angles with *supplementary* angles.

TANGENTS

A tangent to a circle is perpendicular to the radius through the point

Fig. 17.15

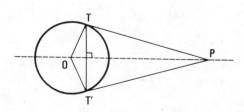

of contact. Two tangents drawn from a point P to a circle are equal in length, and Fig. 17.15 is symmetrical about the line OP. From this we can deduce that TT' is perpendicular to OP.

ALTERNATE SEGMENT THEOREM

The angle between a tangent and the chord through the point of contact is equal to the angle in the alternate segment. There are two angles between the tangent and the chord and two segments (Fig. 17.16).

Fig. 17.16

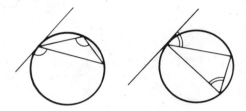

INTERSECTING CHORD THEOREM

If AB and CD are two chords of a circle intersecting at a point O, either inside or outside the circle (Fig. 17.17), then:

$$AO \times OB = CO \times OD$$

Fig. 17.17

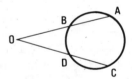

Fig. 17.18

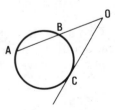

In particular, if one chord is a tangent (Fig. 17.18), then:

$$AO \times OB = CO^2$$

There are several useful numerical calculations based on this theorem.

Specimen question Part of a bridge is to take the form of a circular arc, with a span of 40 m. The highest point of this arc is to be 10 m above the chord through the ends of the arc. Find the radius of the circular arc.

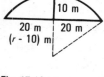

Fig. 17.19

Answer With the notation in Fig. 17.19:

$$AO \times OB = CO \times OD \text{ (intersecting chord theorem)}$$

If the radius of the circle is r metres:

$$20 \times 20 = 10 \times (2r - 10)$$
$$2r - 10 = 40$$
$$r = 25$$

Therefore the radius is 25 metres.

Specimen question Find the distance to the horizon from a point on a balloon drifting over an ocean, 200 m above sea-level.

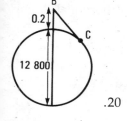

Fig. 17.20

Answer Taking the Earth to be a sphere 6400 km radius, and using Fig. 17.20 (not drawn to scale):

$$BC^2 = 0.2 \times 12\,800.2$$

(We can use 12 800 instead of 12 800.2 without much loss of accuracy.)

$$BC^2 = 2560$$
$$BC = 50.6, \text{ to 3 sf}$$

Therefore the distance to the horizon is about 50.6 km.

EXAMINATION QUESTIONS 17C

1 In Fig. 17.21, angle ABC = 38°. Calculate angles AOC, ACO, ACT.

Fig. 17.21

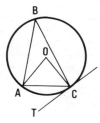

2 In Fig. 17.22, angle ABC is 40°. Calculate angles AOC, ACO, ADC, ACT and ACS.

3 If instead, in Fig. 17.22, angle ABC is known to be between 40° and 46°, find the greatest and least possible sizes of the angles AOC and OCA.

4 A, B and C are three points on a circle centre O. Angles AOB, BOC and AOC are 70°, 50° and 120° respectively. The straight line through O perpendicular to AB meets CB produced at P and meets AC at S. Calculate the angles ACB, OPB and ASP.

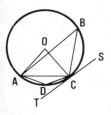

Fig. 17.22

5   In Fig. 17.23, TAS is the tangent to the circle at A. AB is any chord through A, AK bisects the angle TAB, AL bisects the angle BAS. Prove that KL is a diameter of the circle.

Fig. 17.23

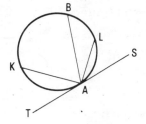

SIMILAR TRIANGLES

Equiangular triangles have corresponding sides proportional. Using Fig. 17.24:

$$\frac{AB}{XY} = \frac{BC}{YZ} = \frac{CA}{ZX}$$

The converse of this theorem is also true, that if corresponding sides are proportional, then the triangles are equiangular.

Fig. 17.24

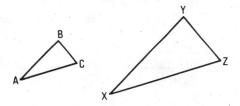

ENLARGEMENT

If the triangles are suitably situated, it is possible to describe one triangle as an enlargement of the other. In Fig. 17.25:

$$\frac{AB}{XY} = \frac{BC}{YZ} = \frac{CA}{ZX} = \frac{1}{3}$$

Triangle ABC has been enlarged, centre O, by a factor of 3. Notice that the ratio OA:OX, etc., is also 1:3, whereas A divides OX in the

Fig. 17.25

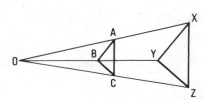

ratio 1:2. Take particular care in using given ratios correctly; this is a common source of error.

Specimen question In triangle ABC (Fig. 17.26), PQ is parallel to BC. AB = 6 cm, PQ = 3 cm and AP:PB = 1:2. Calculate (*a*) the length of BC, (*b*) the ratio of the area triangle APQ:triangle ABC.

Fig. 17.26

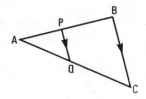

Answer

(*a*) Since PQ is parallel to BC, triangles APQ and ABC are equiangular, so corresponding sides are proportional. It is often helpful to separate the triangles, as in Fig. 17.27.

$$\frac{BC}{PQ} = \frac{AB}{AP}$$

$$\frac{BC}{3} = \frac{6}{2}$$

BC = 9, the length of BC is 9 cm

Fig. 17.27

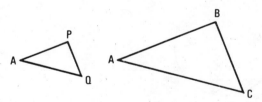

(*b*) The areas of similar figures are proportional to the squares of the corresponding lengths, so that:

$$\frac{\text{area triangle APQ}}{\text{area triangle ABC}} = \left(\frac{1}{3}\right)^2$$

and the ratio of the areas is 1:9.

▶ Remember that the ratio of corresponding volumes of similar solids is the cube of the ratio of corresponding lengths.

1   A straight line parallel to the base BC of the triangle ABC meets AB in X and AC in Y. If AX:XB = 3:4, find the ratios (a) AY:YC, (b) XY:BC.

2   In the parallelogram ABCD, H and K are the points in AD and BC respectively such that AH:HD = 2:1 and BK:KC = 1:3. Lines through H and K parallel to AB meet AC in X and Y respectively. Find the ratios (a) AX:XC, (b) AY:YC, (c) AY:YX, (d) YX:XC.

3   In the square ABCD, E and F are points in AB, BC respectively such that AE:EB = 1:2 and BF:FC = 1:2. The lines AF and DE meet at X. Prove that the triangles AEX, AFB are similar, and that their areas are in the ratio 1:10.

4   A straight tunnel is bored through the Earth, assumed to be a sphere radius 6400 km.
(a)   If the tunnel is 4000 km long, how near does it pass to the centre of the Earth?
(b)   if the tunnel is to pass through a point 2000 km from the centre of the Earth, what is the length of the tunnel?

5   In Fig. 17.28, angle DAX = angle BAC.
(a)   Prove that triangles ABC, AXD are similar.
(b)   Prove that AD.BC = AC.XD.
(c)   Prove that triangles AXB, ADC are similar.
(d)   Prove that AB.CD = AC.XB.
(e)   From (b) and (d), deduce Ptolemy's theorem:

$$AD.BC + AB.CD = AC.BD$$

Fig. 17.28

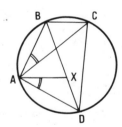

LOCI AND CONSTRUCTIONS

CONTENTS

▶ **Locus**   **193**

▶ **Some useful constructions**   **195**
To reflect a point P in a straight line l 196
To reflect a given straight line m in a given straight
line l 196
To find the centre of rotation   196
To draw the shortest path from a point A to another
point B, going through some one point in straight line l
not through A or B 197

▶ **Examination questions 18**   **197**

LOCUS

A **locus** is a set of points satisfying a given condition. This can be used to define a certain curve, as when a circle is defined as the set of all points equidistant from a fixed point. Some common loci are as follows.

- The set of all points in a plane equidistant from a fixed point is a **circle**.

- The set of all points in space equidistant from a fixed point is a **sphere**.

Fig. 18.1

- The set of all points in a plane equidistant from a fixed (infinite) straight line in that plane is a pair of **parallel infinite straight lines** (Fig 18.1).

- The set of all points in a plane distant d from a fixed (infinite) straight line not in that plane is also a pair of parallel straight lines, but *not* 2d apart.

Fig. 18.2

- In the previous two loci, if we have a finite straight line-segment l, then we have to consider the end points separately. The locus of a point a given distance d from some one point in a line-segment l consists of a **pair of straight lines joined by two semi-circular arcs** (Fig. 18.2).

- The locus in space of a point a fixed distance from a fixed (infinite) straight line is a **circular cylinder**. Again, if we have a line-segment, the locus becomes a **cylinder with spherical ends**.

Fig. 18.3

- The locus of a point in a plane equidistant from two fixed points A, B is the **perpendicular bisector** (sometimes called the mediator) **of the straight line** joining A and B (Fig. 18.3).

Fig. 18.4

- The locus of a point in a plane equidistant from two straight lines in that plane is the **pair of straight lines bisecting the angles** between the two given straight lines (Fig. 18.4).

- The locus of all points P such that a given straight line AB subtends a right angle at P is the **circle on AB as diameter** (Fig. 18.5).

Fig. 18.5

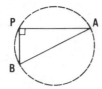

- **Constant angle locus.** The locus of all points P such that a given line-segment AB subtends a constant angle x at P is an arc of a circle through A and B. Strictly, the locus is the arcs of two circles through A and B (Fig. 18.6).

Fig. 18.6

- The locus of all points P such that the sum of the distances from two fixed points A and B is constant is an **ellipse** (Fig. 18.7).

Fig. 18.7

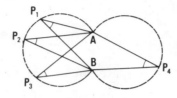

The following examples illustrate questions that are asked in examinations.

Specimen question Mark two points A and B 4 cm apart. If P is a point in the plane of the paper, shade the region in which $AP < PB$.

Fig. 18.8

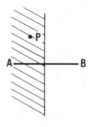

Answer Since the perpendicular bisector of AB is the locus of all points for which $AP = PB$, the half-plane containing A will be the region for which $AP < PB$ (Fig 18.8).

Specimen question Mark two points A and B 6 cm apart. If P is a point in the plane of the paper, shade the outer boundary of the region in which $A\hat{P}B > 50°$.

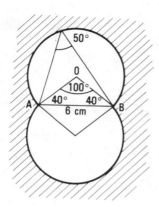

Fig. 18.9

Answer To construct the boundary of the region accurately we need to find the centres of the two circles. Since the angle at the circumference is 50°, the angle at the centre will be 100°, so each angle made by a radius with *AB* will be 40° (Fig. 18.9). Using protractors we can find the two centres and the radius *OA*; we can then draw the two circular arcs. The outer boundary of the region enclosed by those arcs we shade as required.

Specimen question Two points *A* and *B* are 5 cm apart. Find the locus of the point *P* such that the area of the triangle *APB* is 10 cm².

Answer Since the area of a triangle is:

$$\tfrac{1}{2}\,\text{base} \times \text{perpendicular height}$$

the vertex *P* must lie on one of the two straight lines 4 cm from *AB* (Fig. 18.10).

Fig. 18.10

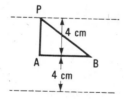

SOME USEFUL CONSTRUCTIONS

To draw the perpendicular bisector (mediator) of the straight line segment *AB*.

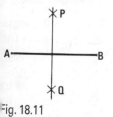

Fig. 18.11

Draw arcs, centres *A* and *B*, radius greater than $\tfrac{1}{2}$ *AB* (Fig. 18.11). If they meet in *P* and *Q*, *PQ* is the perpendicular bisector of *AB*.

**TO REFLECT A POINT *P*
IN A STRAIGHT LINE *l***

Draw an arc of a circle, radius *r* large enough to cut *l*, to meet *l* in *A* and *B* (Fig. 18.12). Centres *A* and *B*, draw arcs radii *r*, to cut at *Q*. Then *Q* is the image of *P* reflected in *l*.

Fig. 18.12

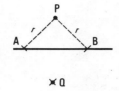

**TO REFLECT A GIVEN
STRAIGHT LINE *m* IN A
GIVEN STRAIGHT LINE *l***

If *l* and *m* intersect on the paper, call the point of intersection *R* (Fig. 18.13). Reflect any one point *P* in the line *l*. If *Q* is the image in *l* of any one point *P* in the line *m*, then *QR* is the image of *m*.

Fig. 18.13

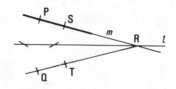

If *l* and *m* do not meet on the paper, find the images *Q* and *T* of any two points *P* and *S* in *l*. Then *QT* is the image of *m*.

**TO FIND THE CENTRE OF
ROTATION**

If *P′* is the image of a point *P* and *Q′* is the image of a point *Q*, the centre *O* of the rotation is the intersection of the perpendicular bisectors of *PP′* and *QQ′* (Fig. 18.14).

Fig. 18.14

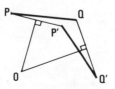

TO DRAW THE SHORTEST PATH FROM A POINT *A* TO ANOTHER POINT *B*, GOING THROUGH SOME ONE POINT IN A STRAIGHT LINE *l* NOT THROUGH *A* OR *B*

If B' is the image in l of B, join AB'. If this meets l in X, AXB is the shortest route (Fig. 18.15).

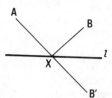

Fig. 18.15

EXAMINATION QUESTIONS 18

1   Draw the triangle ABC in which $AB = 4$ cm, $BC = 5$ cm and $CA = 6$ cm. Construct
   (*a*)   the locus of all points equidistant from A and B;
   (*b*)   the locus of all points equidistant from B and C;
   (*c*)   the locus of all points equidistant from C and A. Verify that these three loci have a common point.

2   Draw the triangle ABC in which $AB = 6$ cm, $ABC = 50°$ and $CAB = 60°$. Construct
   (*a*)   the locus of all points equidistant from AB and BC;
   (*b*)   the locus of all points equidistant from AC and AB;
   (*c*)   the locus of all points equidistant from AC and BC. Verify that these three loci have a common point.

Fig. 18.16

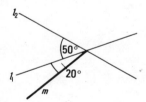

3   In Fig. 18.16 lines l_1 and l_2 intersect at an angle of 50°. The angle between m and l_1 is 20°. If $l_1(m)$ denotes the image of m when reflected in l_1, construct the lines $l_1(m)$ and $l_2(m)$. Find by drawing or calculation the angle made by m with:
   (*a*) $l_2(l_1(m))$;
   (*b*) $l_1(l_2(m))$.

Fig. 18.17

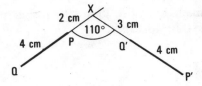

4   In Fig 18.17 $PQ = P'Q' = 4\,$cm, $PX = 2\,$cm, $Q'X = 3\,$cm and angle $Q'XP = 110°$. Construct the centre of the rotation which has transformed PQ into $P'Q'$, and measure the angle of rotation.

NETS OF SOLIDS

CONTENTS

▶ Net of a cube   201

▶ Net of a tetrahedron   201

▶ Net of a cylinder   202

▶ Net of a cone   202

▶ Examination questions 19   203

NET OF A CUBE

The six faces of the cube ABCDXYZW are illustrated in Fig. 19.1. This is the net of the cube. If we wish to make a model of the cube, we could use the net, fold it, then join the appropriate edges together.

Fig. 19.1

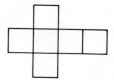

If we tried to use the net shown in Fig 19.2 we should find, however, that when we fold along the edges, one face is repeated and another face of the cube is not formed.

Fig. 19.2

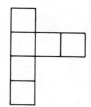

NET OF A TETRAHEDRON

Fig. 19.3(a) shows the net of a regular tetrahedron in which all edges are equal. Whether the tetrahedron is regular or not, X, Y and Z have to be at the midpoints of BC, CA and AB respectively, so that lengths AZ = ZB, BX = XC and CY = YA (Fig. 19.3(b)).

Fig. 19.3

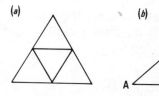

NET OF A CYLINDER

Fig. 19.4 illustrates the net of the cylinder, length l cm, radius r cm. It shows that the total surface area of the cylinder is:

$2\pi rl$ cm^2 for the curved part

and:

Fig. 19.4

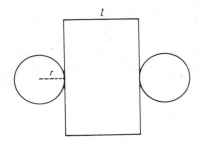

πr^2 cm^2 for each of the two ends

making a total of:

$$(2\pi rl + 2\pi r^2) \text{ cm}^2 = 2\pi r(r+l) \text{ cm}^2$$

NET OF A CONE

Fig. 19.5 illustrates the net of a cone, base radius r cm, slant height l cm. It can be shown that the total surface area is:

$$\pi r^2 + \pi rl \text{ cm}^2 = \pi r(r+l) \text{ cm}^2$$

Fig. 19.5

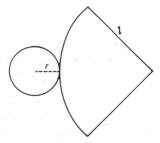

Specimen question Fig. 19.6 shows the net of a triangular prism. When folded to form the prism, which points will join with point

(a)   G,

(b)   D?

Fig. 19.6

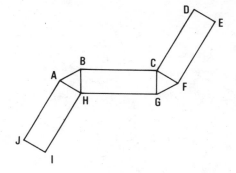

Answer Folding the prism as in Fig. 19.7, we see that:

Fig. 19.7

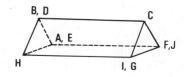

(a)   G joins to I;
(b)   D joins to B.

1   Name the solids of which Figs 19.8(*a*), (*b*), (*c*) and (*d*) are the nets, and illustrate each of these with a sketch.

Fig. 19.8

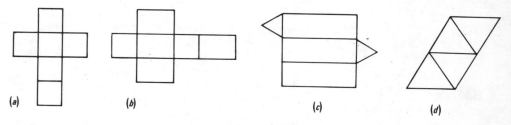

(*a*)   (*b*)   (*c*)   (*d*)

2   Draw a net of each of the following solids.
(*a*)   A pyramid on a square base, side 3 cm, each slant edge length 4 cm (Fig. 19.9(*a*)).
(*b*)   A tetrahedron, edge 5 cm (Fig. 19.9(*b*)).
(*c*)   A regular octohedron, edge 4 cm (Fig 19.9(*c*)).
(*d*)   A cube, edge 4 cm, with two pyramids, slant edges 6 cm (Fig. 19.9(*d*)).

Fig. 19.9

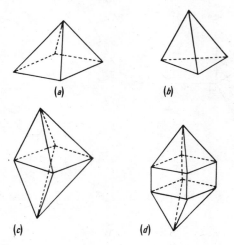

3   Correct each of the figures in Figs 19.10(a), (b) and (c) so that it could be the net of a solid. Name the solid in each case.

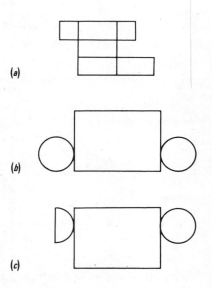

Fig. 19.10

TRIGONOMETRY: DEFINITIONS, RIGHT-ANGLED TRIANGLES

CONTENTS

▶ **Summary** 207

▶ **Definitions** 209

▶ **The trigonometric functions** 210

▶ **Examination questions 20A** 211

▶ **Making a right-angled triangle by drawing a perpendicular** 211

▶ **Angles of elevation and depression** 213

▶ **Shortest distance to a straight line** 214

▶ **Examination questions 20B** 215

SUMMARY

In Fig. 20.1:

► $\sin = \dfrac{\text{opposite}}{\text{hypotenuse}}$, or the projection onto Oy

► $\cos = \dfrac{\text{adjacent}}{\text{hypotenuse}}$, or the projection onto Ox

► $\tan = \dfrac{\text{opposite}}{\text{adjacent}}$, or $\dfrac{\sin}{\cos}$

Fig. 20.1

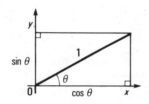

► $\cot = \dfrac{1}{\tan}$

► $\sec = \dfrac{1}{\cos}$

► $\csc = \dfrac{1}{\sin}$

► **Some useful results:**

$\sin 0° = \cos 90° = 0$

$\sin 30° = \cos 60° = \tfrac{1}{2}$

$\sin 45° = \cos 45° = \dfrac{1}{\sqrt{2}}$

$\sin 60° = \cos 30° = \tfrac{1}{2}\sqrt{3}$

$\sin 90° = \cos 0° = 1$

$\sin^2 A + \cos^2 A = 1$, for all angles A

► **Sine formula:**

$$\frac{a}{\sin A} = \frac{b}{\sin B} = \frac{c}{\sin C} = 2R$$

♦ **Cosine formula:**
$$a^2 = b^2 + c^2 - 2bc \cos A$$
i.e. $\cos A = \dfrac{b^2 + c^2 - a^2}{2bc}$

♦ **Area of triangle** $= \frac{1}{2}bc \sin A$
$= \sqrt{\{s(s-a)(s-b)(s-c)\}}$,
where $s = \frac{1}{2}(a+b+c)$
In Fig. 20.2:

♦ **length s of an arc** $= \dfrac{\theta}{360}(2\pi r)$

♦ **area of a sector** $= \dfrac{\theta}{360}(\pi r^2)$.

Fig. 20.2

♦ **Graph of sin** – see Fig. 20.3
♦ **Graph of cos** – see Fig. 20.4.
♦ **Graph of tan** – see Fig. 20.5.

Fig. 20.3

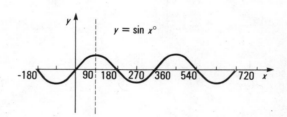

Fig. 20.4

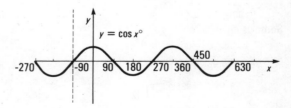

Fig. 20.5

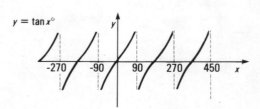

DEFINITIONS

Equiangular triangles have corresponding sides proportional (Fig. 20.6), so if one angle in each triangle is known to be a right angle (Fig. 20.7) then, when a second angle is given, the three angles of the triangle are determined, and hence the ratio of pairs of corresponding sides. Considering one of the angles, A, we define the ratios:

Fig. 20.6

Fig. 20.7

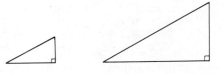

- sine $A = \dfrac{\text{opposite}}{\text{hypotenuse}}$

- cosine $A = \dfrac{\text{adjacent}}{\text{hypotenuse}}$

- tangent $A = \dfrac{\text{opposite}}{\text{adjacent}}$

Using Fig. 20.8, we have:

$$\sin A = \tfrac{9}{41}$$
$$\cos A = \tfrac{40}{41}$$
$$\tan A = \tfrac{9}{40}$$

Fig. 20.8

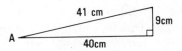

When finding the trigonometric ratios, it may help to label the sides of the triangle, as in Fig. 20.9. Start with the given angle A, and label the longest side the hypotenuse; the side next to the angle is the adjacent side, then the third side is that opposite the angle in which we are interested.

Fig. 20.9

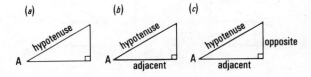

Once any one ratio has been found, the angles of the triangle can be obtained, either using a calculator or from tables. In this example:

$$\sin A = \tfrac{9}{41} = 0.2195$$

$\therefore A = 12.68°$ by calculator or $12°\ 41'$ from tables. Calculators are much easier to use than tables, but if one is not available then of course tables must be used.

NB If using cosine tables, remember to subtract the difference.

Specimen question Find
(*a*)   cos 38° 40′
(*b*)   the angle whose cosine is 0.8600.

Answer

(i) Using calculator set in degrees,

(*a*) $40' = \dfrac{40}{60}°$

$\therefore \cos (38\tfrac{40}{60})° = 0.7808$

(*b*)   inv cos 0.8600 = 30.68°

(ii) (*a*)   From the tables:

$$\cos 38°\ 36' = 0.7815$$
$$\text{the difference for } 4' = \qquad 7$$

$$\therefore \qquad \cos 38°\ 40' = 0.7808$$

(*b*)   From tables:

$$0.8607 = \cos 30°\ 36'$$
$$7 = \text{the difference for } 5'$$
$$0.8600 = \cos 30°\ 41'$$

THE TRIGONOMETRIC FUNCTIONS

If we are using only angles between 0° and 90°, then not only does 'sine' associate every angle with one and only one number (Fig. 20.10(*a*)), but every number (between 0 and 1) is associated with one and only one angle (Fig. 20.10(*b*)). Thus 'sine' can be described as a function which also has an inverse. This inverse function is usually written $\sin^{-1}$, though inv sin and arc sin are often shown on many calculators. If the domain is the set of angles between 0° and 90°, the range is the set of numbers from 0 to 1. Similarly with cosine and with tangent, though in the latter case the range is the whole set of non-negative numbers.

Fig. 20.10

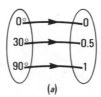

(*a*)

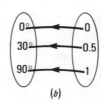

(*b*)

1 Check your use of calculator or tables by finding:
  (a)   sin 21.4°
  (b)   cos 31.4°
  (c)   tan 41.4°
  (d)   sin 51° 40'
  (e)   cos 61° 40'
  (f)   tan 71° 40'

2 'The angle whose sine is . . .' is often abbreviated $\sin^{-1}$ or arc sin or inv sin. Find:
  (a)   the angle whose sine is 0.1
  (b) $\sin^{-1}(0.2)$
  (c)   inv sin $(\frac{1}{3})$
  (d)   the angle whose cosine is 0.4
  (e)   inv cos (0.5)
  (f)   arc cos $(\frac{2}{3})$
  (g)   the angle whose tangent is 0.7
  (h)   arc tan (0.8)
  (i)   inv tan $(\frac{4}{3})$

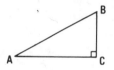

Fig. 20.11

3 Use Fig. 20.11.
  (a)   If AB = 8 cm and A = 41°, find AC and BC.
  (b)   If AB = 8 cm and BC = 6.5 cm, find angle A then AC.
  (c)   If AB = 12 cm and AC = 10 cm, find angle A then BC.
  (d)   If AC = 8 cm and BC = 7 cm, find angle A then AB.

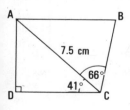

Fig. 20.12

In question **3** of the above, angle C = 90°. In many problems set in examinations, we have to make a right-angled triangle by drawing a perpendicular.

Specimen question In Fig. 20.12 angle BAD = angle ADC = 90°, angle ACB = 66° and angle ACD = 41°. The length of AC = 7.5 cm. Calculate the lengths of AD and AB.

Answer We can find the length of AD easily as triangle ADC contains a right angle at D. Thus:

$$\sin 41° = \frac{AD}{7.5},$$

$$\therefore AD = 7.5 \sin 41°$$

$$= 4.920, \text{ to three decimal places}$$

Fig. 20.13

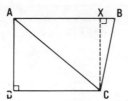

Since there is not a right angle in triangle ABC, the easiest way to find the length of AB is to draw the line through C perpendicular to AB to meet AB in X (Fig. 20.13). Then:

$$AX = CD = 7.5 \cos 41° = 5.660$$

and:

$$BX = CX \tan 17° = 1.504$$
$$AB = 5.660 + 1.504 = 7.164$$

Alternatively, a line AY can be drawn through A perpendicular to BC and the right-angled triangles ACY, ABY used (see p.220).

Specimen question A man walks 50 m on a bearing of 050°, then 40 m on a bearing of 120°. Calculate the distance from his starting point O, and the bearing of his final position from his starting point.

Fig. 20.14

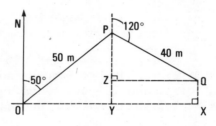

Answer Draw perpendiculars as in Fig 20.14. The distance that Q is east of O is OY+YX. To find OY, in triangle OPY, angle OPY = 50° so that:

$$\sin 50° = \frac{OY}{50}$$

and OY = 50 sin 50° = 38.30. In triangle PQZ, angle QPZ = 60° so that:

$$\sin 60° = \frac{ZQ}{40}$$

and ZQ = 40 sin 60° = 34.64. Thus his distance east of O is:

$$(34.64 + 38.30) \text{ m} = 72.94 \text{ m}$$

His distance north of O is QX, and QX = PY−PZ. Now:

$$\cos 50° = \frac{PY}{50}$$

so PY = 50 cos 50° = 32.14 and similarly PZ = 40 cos 60° = 20. So his distance north of O is:

$$(32.14-20)\,m = 12.14\,m$$

Applying Pythagoras' theorem to triangle OQX (Fig. 20.15), we have:

$$OQ^2 = (72.94)^2 + (12.14)^2$$
$$\simeq 5467$$
$$OQ \simeq 74$$

the distance of Q from O is 74 m. To find the bearing of Q from O:

$$\tan QOX = \frac{12.14}{72.94}$$

so angle QOX $\simeq$ 9° and the bearing of Q from O is 081°.

20.15

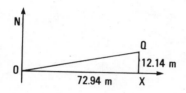

NGLES OF ELEVATION AND DEPRESSION

The angle of elevation of an object B from an observer A who is below the level of B is the angle which the line AB makes with the horizontal (Fig. 20.16(a)). If C is below A, the angle of depression of C from A is the angle which AC makes with the horizontal (Fig. 20.16(b)).

20.16

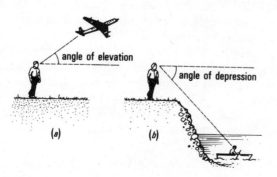

(a)   (b)

NB Notice that both angles are measured with the horizontal and that the angle of elevation of B from A is equal to the angle of depression of A from B.

Specimen question A man M on the top of a cliff 60 m high sees tw
buoys A and B whose angles of depression are 15.2° and 12.5°. T
line AB is perpendicular to the plane of the cliff. What is the distan
between the two buoys?

Fig. 20.17

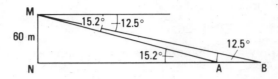

Answer Let MN represent the plane face of the cliff (Fig. 20.17). Then

$$\tan 15.2° = \frac{60}{AN}$$

so:

$$AN = \frac{60}{\tan 15.2°} = 221$$

and:

$$\tan 12.5° = \frac{60}{BN}$$

so:

$$BN = \frac{60}{\tan 12.5°} = 271$$

Thus:

$$AB = 271 - 221 = 50,\text{ the distance between the buoys is}$$
metres.

SHORTEST DISTANCE TO A STRAIGHT LINE

The shortest distance from a point P to a given straight line l is t
perpendicular from P on to l. This can be applied to many trigonom
rical problems. If a boat starts from a mooring M 5 km due north o
rock R, and sails on a bearing of 160° (Fig. 20.18(a)), its short
distance from the rock will be 5 sin 20° km, i.e. about 1.71 km. If
safety reasons the boat must not come within 0.5 km of the rock, t
region into which the boat must not sail is circular (Fig. 20.18(b)) a
the critical angle is the angle RMQ where:

$$\sin RMQ = \frac{0.5}{5} = 0.1$$

i.e. $R\hat{M}Q = 5.7°$

ig. 20.18

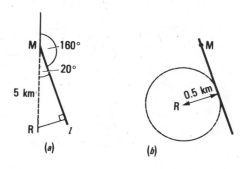

(a)   (b)

1   In triangle ABC, BC = 9.4 cm, angle BAC = 40° and angle BCA = 30°. Draw the line through B perpendicular to AC to meet AC at X. Calculate
   (a)   BX,
   (b)   AB,
   (c)   CX,
   (d)   CA.

2   A man whose eyes are 1.8 m above the ground is 60 m from a vertical flagpole, height 20 m. Find:
   (a)   the angle of elevation of the top of the flagpole from the man's eyes;
   (b)   the angle of elevation from the man's eyes of a knot halfway up the flagpole.

3   A point T is 10 km due north of a point R. A point S is 8 km from T, and the bearing of S from T is 130°. Find the distance of S from R and the bearing of S from R.

4   Points A, B and C lie in a straight line, such that AB = 220 m and BC = 170 m. A vertical tower BT at B is such that the angle of elevation of the top of the tower T from A is 10°. Find the angle of elevation of T from C.

5   An observer O is placed on a straight road running east–west. A gun G is 4 km from O, on a bearing of 070°. If shells from the gun can just reach the road, calculate the range of the gun. If, however, the range is 2 km, find the length of roadway within range of the gun.

INE AND COSINE
ORMULAE;
HREE-DIMENSIONAL
ROBLEMS

CONTENTS

▶ **Summary** 219

▶ **Sine formula** 219

▶ **Cosine formula** 221

▶ **To solve triangles that do not have a right angle** 221

▶ **Note on the use of calculators** 222

▶ **Examination questions 21A** 223

▶ **Latitude and longitude** 223

▶ **Examination questions 21B** 224

▶ **Three-dimensional problems** 224

▶ **Examination questions 21C** 226

MMARY

▶ **Sine formula**
In any triangle ABC

$$\frac{a}{\sin A} = \frac{b}{\sin B} = \frac{c}{\sin C}$$

▶ **Cosine formula**
$$a^2 = b^2 + c^2 - 2bc \cos A$$

▶ **Circle of latitude**
The radius of the circle of latitude λ is R cos λ, where R is the radius of the Earth (about 6400 km).

▶ **Three-dimensional problems**
The angle α between a line and a plane (Fig. 21.1(b)).

21.1(a)
angle β between two
nes is the angle
ween lines in each
ne perpendicular to the
mmon line of the planes.

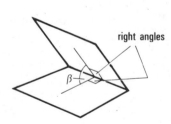

right angles

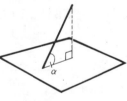

Fig. 21.1(b)

NE FORMULA

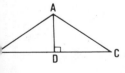

. 21.2

Using Fig. 21.2, in which AD is perpendicular to BC, from triangle ABD, AD = AB sin B and from triangle ACD, AD = AC sin C, so that:

$$\frac{b}{\sin B} = \frac{c}{\sin C}$$

Similarly, drawing a line through B perpendicular to AC:

$$\frac{a}{\sin A} = \frac{c}{\sin C}$$

whence:

$$\frac{a}{\sin A} = \frac{b}{\sin B} = \frac{c}{\sin C}$$

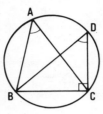

Fig. 21.3

For an alternative proof, draw the circumcircle of triangle ABC a then the diameter through B (Fig. 21.3). From triangle BCD, an BDC = angle A (angles in same segment) and angle BCD = 90° (an in a semicircle), so that BC = BD sin BDC, i.e.

$$2R = \frac{a}{\sin A}$$

where R is the radius of the circumcircle. Similarly:

$$2R = \frac{b}{\sin B}$$

and:

$$2R = \frac{c}{\sin C}$$

so that:

$$\frac{a}{\sin A} = \frac{b}{\sin B} = \frac{c}{\sin C} = 2R$$

The symmetry of this result should be noticed.

Specimen question Using the data in the specimen question on page 2 find AB using the sine formula (see Fig. 21.4).

Fig. 21.4

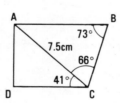

Answer In triangle ABC:

$$\frac{AB}{\sin 66°} = \frac{7.5}{\sin 73°}$$

$$\therefore AB = 7.16, \text{ to three sf}$$

COSINE FORMULA

In Fig. 21.5, BD is perpendicular to AC; denote the length AD by x. Then with the usual notation:

$$DC = b-x$$

Fig. 21.5

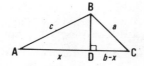

From triangle ABD:

$$BD^2 = c^2 - x^2$$

and from triangle BCD:

$$BD^2 = a^2 - (b-x)^2$$

whence:

$$c^2 - x^2 = a^2 - (b-x)^2$$

so that:

$$c^2 = a^2 - b^2 + 2bx$$

but:

$$x = c \cos A$$

so:

$$a^2 = b^2 + c^2 - 2bc \cos A$$

This formula enables us to find the third side of a triangle, knowing two sides and the included angle. To find one **angle** of a triangle, change the subject of the equation so that:

$$\cos A = \frac{b^2 + c^2 - a^2}{2bc}$$

TO SOLVE TRIANGLES THAT DO NOT HAVE A RIGHT ANGLE

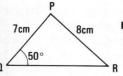

Fig. 21.6

- Given two sides and one not-included angle, or two angles and one side, **use the sine formula**.
- Given three sides, or two sides and the included angle, **use the cosine formula**.

Specimen question In triangle PQR (Fig. 21.6), PQ = 7 cm, PR = 8 cm and angle PQR = 50°. Calculate the angle PRQ.

Answer Using the sine formula:

$$\frac{7}{\sin PRQ} = \frac{8}{\sin 50°}$$

$$\sin PRQ = \frac{7 \sin 50°}{8}$$

$$\therefore \text{angle } PRQ = 42°$$

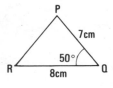

Fig. 21.7

Specimen question In triangle PQR (Fig. 21.7), PQ = 7 cm, QR = 8 cm and angle PQR = 50°. Find the length of PR and the angle QPR.

Answer

$$PR^2 = PQ^2 + QR^2 - 2 \times PQ \times QR \cos 50°$$
$$= 7^2 + 8^2 - 2 \times 7 \times 8 \cos 50°$$
$$= 49 + 64 - 71.99$$
$$= 41.01$$
$$PR = 6.404, \text{ to 4 sf}$$

NB Take care to find first the product $2 \times 7 \times 8 \cos 50°$, then subtract it from $7^2 + 8^2$; it is only too easy to make the mistake of calculating $(7^2 + 8^2 - 2 \times 7 \times 8) \cos 50°$.

To find angle QPR, use the sine formula:

$$\frac{\sin QPR}{8} = \frac{\sin 50°}{6.404}$$

$$\sin QPR = \frac{8 \sin 50°}{6.404}$$

$$\therefore Q\hat{P}R = 73.1°$$

We could have used the cosine formula, in the form:

$$\cos QPR = \frac{7^2 + (6.404)^2 - 8^2}{2 \times 7 \times 6.404}$$

but the calculations of the sine formula are usually easier to carry out, whether using a calculator or not.

NOTE ON THE USE OF CALCULATORS

Always set out clearly, as above, the calculations being performed on the calculator. This enables you to see exactly what calculations you are carrying out, and enables an examiner to follow your working. It is, of course, always important to carry out a rough check of your calculations, and to beware of ambiguity in the use of the inv sin function (see question **2** below).

EXAMINATION QUESTIONS 21A

1 In triangle ABC, AB = 8.4 cm, angle B = 44° and angle C = 64°. Find angle A and the lengths of the other two sides.

2 In triangle ABC, AB = 8.4 cm, BC = 7.4 cm and angle A = 40°. Use the sine formula to find angle ACB, given that this angle is acute, and then find angle ABC and the length of AC.

   Make a scale drawing to show that there are two possible triangles that can be drawn from the data, and that in one of them angle ACB is obtuse. Calculate angle ABC and the length of AC in this case.

3 In triangle ABC, AB = 8 cm, BC = 7 cm and AC = 5 cm. Calculate the angles of the triangle.

4 In triangle ABC, AB = 8.4 cm, BC = 7.8 cm and angle ABC = 80°. Calculate the length of AC and the angles A and C in the triangle.

LATITUDE AND LONGITUDE

In Fig. 21.8, N and S represent the north and south poles. The line SN is the axis of the Earth. The circle BQA represents the equator.

Fig. 21.8

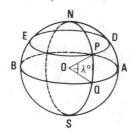

- A **great circle** is a section of the Earth's surface by any plane through the centre O.
- The **shortest distance** between two points on the surface of the earth is the minor arc of the great circle through those two points.
- A **meridian of longitude** is a great circle (here NPQS) which passes through the north and south poles.
- A **parallel of latitude** is a section of the Earth's surface by a plane parallel to the equator (here DPE).

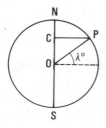
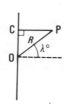

Fig. 21.9

Looking at the section of the Earth in Fig. 21.9 we see that the radius of a circle of latitude angle λ is $R \cos \lambda$, where R is the radius of the Earth.

Specimen question An aeroplane is to fly from a point P 35°N 30°E to a point Q 35°N 150°W (Fig. 21.10). Find the length (*a*) of the path over the north pole, (*b*) the path along the circle of latitude 35°N.

Fig. 21.10

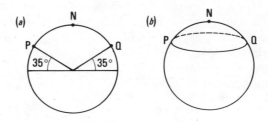

Answer The path over the north pole is part of a great circle. Since it subtends an angle 110° at the centre, the length of the path is:

$$\frac{110}{360} \times 2\pi R$$

where R is the radius of the Earth. Taking R to be 6400 km, the length of the path over the north pole is 12 300 km, to 3 sf.
    The path around the circle of latitude 35°N is exactly half the circumference of that circle (from 30°E to 150°W is 180°), so the length of the path around the circle latitude is:

$$\tfrac{1}{2} \times 2\pi R \cos 35° = 16\,500 \text{ km, to 3 sf}$$

EXAMINATION QUESTIONS 21B

(Taking the radius of the Earth to be 6400 km.)

1   Two towns on the equator differ in longitude by 34°. Find the distance between them, along the equator.
2   Two towns on latitude 40°S differ in longitude by 34°. Find the distance between them along the circle of latitude.
3   Two towns on latitude 20°S differ in longitude by 180°. Find the distance between them (*a*) over the south pole, (*b*) around the circle of latitude 20°S.

THREE-DIMENSIONAL PROBLEMS

A straight line perpendicular to a plane is perpendicular to every line in the plane (Fig. 21.11(*a*)). Thus an edge of a rectangular box is perpendicular to every line in the face adjacent to that edge (Fig. 21.11(*b*)), and any line drawn through the vertex of a pyramid perpendicular to the base is perpendicular to every line in the base (Fig. 21.11(c)).

Fig. 21.11

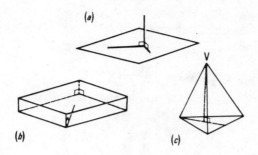

(a)

(b)   (c)

Specimen question Fig. 21.12 shows a right prism whose cross-section is an isosceles triangle ABC. AB = BC = 12 cm; angle ABC = 44°. Find the angle made by AE with the horizontal plane ACFD.

Fig. 21.12

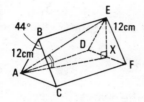

Answer Draw the line EX perpendicular to the plane ACFD. Then triangle DEX has a right angle at X, so that:

$$\sin 22° = \frac{DX}{12}$$

$$DX = 12 \sin 22° = 4.495$$

Similarly, EX = 12 cos 22° = 11.13. From triangle ADX:

$$AX^2 = 16^2 + (4.495)^2$$
$$AX = 16.62$$

But angle AXE is also a right angle, so:

$$\tan EAX = \frac{11.12}{16.62}$$
$$EAX = 34°, \text{ to the nearest degree.}$$

Specimen question Fig. 21.13 shows a pyramid whose base ABC is an equilateral triangle. AB = BC = CA = 6 cm; VA = VB = VC = 8 cm. Find (a) the angle made by the edge VA with the base, (b) the angle made by the face VBC with the base.

ig. 21.13

Answer Draw VG perpendicular to the base to meet the base at G. Then G can be shown (and can be assumed in an examination) to be at the point at which the medians of the triangle ABC meet. Using Fig. 21.14(*a*), AD = 6 cos 30° = 5.196, so AG = $\frac{2}{3}$AD = 3.464. From Fig. 21.14(*b*), the angle made by the edge VA with the base is angle VAG, where:

$$\cos VAG = \frac{3.464}{8}$$

VAG = 64°, to the nearest degree.

Fig. 21.14

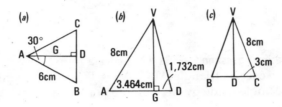

The angle made by the face VBC with the base is angle VDA (Fig. 21.14(*b*)). Applying Pythagoras' theorem to triangle VBD, DV = 7.416, so:

$$\cos VDA = \frac{1.732}{7.416}$$

VDA = 76°, to the nearest degree.

EXAMINATION QUESTIONS 21C

1   A road sign is in the form of a vertical equilateral triangle ABC (Fig. 21.15), with AC horizontal and length 1 m. When the angle of elevation of the sun is 40° and the rays are at right angles to AC, the shadow of B is at point B', a point on the horizontal plane through AC. Find the distance of B' from AC.

Fig. 21.15

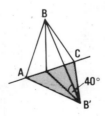

2   Fig. 21.16 shows a pyramid, vertex V, on a square base ABCD. Each side of the square is 4 cm long, and the edges through V are each 5 cm long. Find by calculation the angle made by the edge VA with the base, and the angle made by the face VAB with the base.

Fig. 21.16

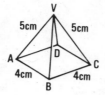

3   Descending a hill of gradient 20°, a skier travels in a straight line which makes an angle of 45° with the line of greatest slope (Fig. 21.17). Find the angle between his path and the horizontal. (*Hint:* suppose that he travels 100 m down his path. Find the distance travelled in the direction of the line of greatest slope, and then the vertical distance he has descended.)

Fig. 21.17

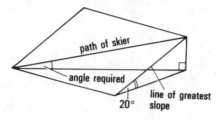

SETS AND SET NOTATION

CONTENTS

▶ **Summary** 231

▶ **Definitions** 232
Geometrical applications 232

▶ **De Morgan's laws** 233

▶ **Examination questions 22** 234

SUMMARY

- $\{\ \}$ the set of
- $n(A)$ the number of elements in the set A
- $\{x:\ \}$ the set of elements x such that
- $\in$ is an element of
- $\notin$ is not an element of
- $\mathscr{E}$ (or $\mathcal{U}$)   the universal set
- $\varnothing$ the empty (null) set
- $\cup$ union
- $\cap$ intersection
- $\subset$ is a subset of
- A' the complement of the set A
- PQ the operation Q followed by the operation P
- $f{:}x \mapsto y$ the function mapping the set X (the domain) into the set Y (the range)
- f^{-1} the inverse of the function f
- $\mathbf{R}$ the set of all real numbers
- $\mathbf{Z}$ the set of all integers
- $\mathbf{Z}_+$ the set of all positive integers
- $\mathbf{Q}$ the set of all rationals, e.g. $\frac{3}{4}$
- A **set** is a well-defined class of objects, so that we can tell without ambiguity whether any one object does or does not belong to that class.
- The **empty** (or **null**) set is the set without any elements.
- Any element(s) chosen from a set form a **subset** of that set; all subsets except the set itself and the empty set are called **proper** subsets.
- Those elements common to two sets A, B, form a set called the **intersection** of A and B, written $A \cap B$; those elements in either A or B or both form a set called the **union** of A and B, written $A \cup B$.
- The **complement** of a set A is the set of all elements in the universal set $\mathscr{E}$ which are not in A, and is denoted by A'.
- The **cardinal number** of a set A is the number of elements in A, and is written $n(A)$. (Sometimes $n\{A\}$ is used.)
- A **relation** associates an element x of one set (the **domain** D) with one or more elements y of another set (the **range** R). The range can be the same set as the domain.
- The element y is the **image** of x under that relation.
- A **function** (mapping) is a relation under which every element in D has one and only one image in R, i.e. it is a one–one or a many–one relation.
- A composite function fg is one in which first g maps an element x into $g(x)$, then f maps $g(x)$ into $fg(x)$. The inverse function is $g^{-1}f^{-1}$.

DEFINITIONS

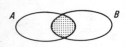

Fig. 22.1

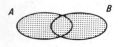

Fig. 22.2

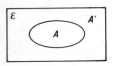

Fig: 22.3

A **set** is a well-defined class of objects, by which we mean that we can tell whether any one object does or does not belong to the set. Thus we can define 'the set of all even numbers', since we know how to test whether a number is even or not, but we cannot define 'the set of all large numbers' as we do not know whether a number is 'large' or not. The members of a set are called its elements, and when listed are often written inside curly brackets, e.g.

The set of all positive numbers less than 10 = {2, 4, 6, 8}

Any elements chosen from a set form a **subset** of that set. Elements common to two sets A and B form a set called the **intersection** of A and B, written $A \cap B$ (Fig. 22.1). Those elements in either A or B (or both) form a set called the **union** of A and B, written $A \cup B$ (Fig. 22.2).

Those elements in the universal set $\mathscr{E}$ that are not in a given set A form a subset A', the **complement** of A (Fig. 22.3).

The number of elements in a set is the cardinal number of the set, written $n\{A\}$ or sometimes $n(A)$. Many examination questions test knowledge of either the properties of numbers or elementary geometry, and require as a start the listing of elements in given sets.

Specimen question If the universal set $\mathscr{E}$ = {integers $n : 4 \leqslant n \leqslant 20$} P = {primes}, A = {multiples of 2}, and B = {multiples of 3}, list the elements in each of the sets (a) P (b) A (c) A' (d) $A' \cap B'$ (e) $(A \cup B)'$.

Answers Since $\mathscr{E}$ is the set of integers between 4 and 20 inclusive:
(a) $P = \{5, 7, 11, 13, 17, 19\}$
(b) $A = \{4, 6, 8, 10, 12, 14, 16, 18, 20\}$
(c) $A' = \{5, 7, 9, 11, 13, 15, 17, 19\}$
(d)   Those elements of A' that are also elements of B' are the elements in $A' \cap B'$. So:

$$A' \cap B' = \{5, 7, 11, 13, 17, 19\}$$

(e)   The elements of B are {6, 9, 12, 15, 18} and $(A \cup B)'$ is the set of elements not in either A or B (or both), i.e.

$$(A \cup B)' = \{5, 7, 11, 13, 17, 19\} \text{ the same set as } A' \cap B'$$

GEOMETRICAL APPLICATIONS

Fig. 22.4

An isosceles triangle has two sides equal; an equilateral triangle has all three sides equal. These definitions are now generally interpreted so that all equilateral triangles are regarded as isosceles triangles. The relation between I, the set of all isosceles triangles and T, the set of all equilateral triangles, is illustrated by the Venn diagram in Fig. 22.4.

Similarly a rhombus (all sides equal in length as well as opposite sides being parallel) is a special case of a parallelogram, just as a square is a special case of a rectangle. The relation between some sets are illustrated in Fig. 22.5, where:

$$H = \{\text{all rhombuses}\}$$
$$P = \{\text{all parallelograms}\}$$
$$R = \{\text{all rectangles}\}$$
$$S = \{\text{all squares}\}$$
$$C = \{\text{all cyclic quadrilaterals}\}$$

Fig. 22.5

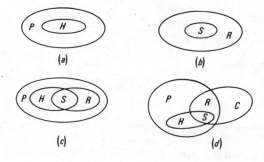

(a)

(b)

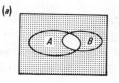

(c)

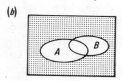

(d)

DE MORGAN'S LAWS

The result in part (e) of the specimen question above illustrates one of de Morgan's laws, which are:

$$(A \cap B)' = A' \cup B',$$
$$(A \cup B)' = A' \cap B',$$

and can be illustrated by Venn diagrams. In Fig. 22.6(a) the shaded region represents either $(A \cap B)'$ or $A' \cup B'$, and in Fig. 22.6(b) the shaded region represents either $(A \cup B)'$ or $A' \cap B'$).

Fig. 22.6

(a)

(b)

In a similar manner, Venn diagrams can be used to show that the operations of forming the union or the intersection of sets are commutative, associative and distributive.

Commutative:

$$A \cup B = B \cup A \text{ and } A \cap B = B \cap A$$

Associative:

$$A \cup (B \cup C) = (A \cup B) \cup C \text{ and } A \cap (B \cap C) = (A \cap B) \cap C$$

♦ That union is **distributive** over intersection, i.e.

$$A \cup (B \cap C) = (A \cup B) \cap (A \cup C)$$

is illustrated by the shaded region in Fig. 22.7(a).

♦ That intersection is **distributive** over union, i.e.

$$A \cap (B \cup C) = (A \cap B) \cup (A \cup C)$$

is illustrated by the shaded region in Fig. 22.7(b).

Fig. 22.7

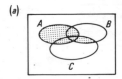 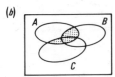

EXAMINATION QUESTIONS 22

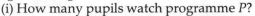

1   If $\mathscr{E} = \{$all integers $n : 1 \leqslant n \leqslant 12\}$, $A = \{$multiples of 2$\}$, $B = \{$multiples of 4$\}$, and $P = \{$primes$\}$, list the elements in (a) A (b) B (c) $A \cap B$ (d) $P \cap A'$. (Remember that 1 is not a prime.)
    Find also (e) $n(P)$ (f) $n(P \cap B)$.

2   If $\mathscr{E} = \{$all triangles$\}$, $I = \{$all isosceles triangles$\}$, and $R = \{$all right-angled triangles$\}$, draw a Venn diagram to illustrate the relation between the sets. Find the angles in all triangles in the set $I \cap R$.

3   Thirty pupils were asked which of the television programmes P and Q they watch. Some of the information obtained is represented in the Venn diagram in Fig. 22.8.
    (i) How many pupils watch programme P?
    (ii) How many watch only one of the programmes P and Q?
    (iii) How many watch neither?   [*NEA specimen question*]

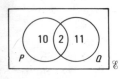

Fig. 22.8

4   Nineteen girls are employed in an office. The Venn diagram in Fig. 22.9 shows some details about the number who can do audio-typing (A), shorthand-typing (S) and use the word-processor (W). They all have at least one of these skills.

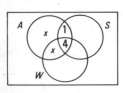

Fig. 22.9

(a)   Eleven girls can do audio-typing. Find x.
(b)   If six girls cannot do either method of typing, how many can do shorthand-typing?
(c)   Nobody does only shorthand-typing. Find:
    (i) how many can use the word-processor;
    (ii) how many can both use the word-processor and do shorthand-typing.
(d)   Copy the Venn diagram and shade the region $W \cap A' \cap S'$. Give a brief description of this set.   [*SEG specimen question*]

RELATIONS AND FUNCTIONS

CONTENTS

▶ **Relations**   237

▶ **Function**   237
Mapping   238
Inverse function   238
Composite function   239

▶ **Examination questions 23**   240

RELATIONS

A relation associates some members of one set (the **domain**) with some members of another set (the **co-domain**), and can often be illustrated by a Papy graph.

Suppose the domain is the set {2,3} and the co-domain is the set {4,5,6}. If the relation is 'less than', then the association between the elements of the domain and the co-domain is illustrated by Fig. 23.1. If the relation 'is a factor of' then the relation is illustrated by Fig. 23.2.

Fig. 23.1

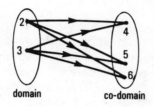

domain   co-domain

Fig. 23.2

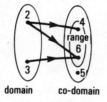

domain   co-domain

Notice in the first relation every element of the co-domain is associated with some one element of the domain, whereas in the second relation the element 5 is not associated with any element of the domain. Those elements in the co-domain which are associated with elements in the domain are said to form the **range** under that relation.

FUNCTION

If the relation is 'one less than' then every element in the domain is associated with one and only one element in the range. The association is now called a **function**.

Many of the functions we study can be described algebraically. The function which associates every element in the domain with the element two greater than it is most simply written $f:x \mapsto x+2$; the function which associates every element with its square is written $f:x \mapsto x^2$. The Papy graphs of functions can be easily recognized because only one arrow goes from each member of the domain. The function $f:x \mapsto x+2$ is illustrated in Fig. 23.3, the domain being $\{1,2,3\}$.

Fig. 23.3

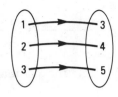

MAPPING

This term should mean exactly the same as function, but is sometimes incorrectly used to mean 'relation', and so is best avoided.

INVERSE FUNCTION

The function $f:x \mapsto x+2$ associated every member of a given domain with the corresponding member of the range. The inverse function associates every member of the range with the corresponding member of the domain (Fig. 23.4). Here the inverse function, written f^{-1}, is such that $f^{-1}:x \mapsto x-2$. Where there may be any confusion, we can refer to elements in the range as y, so that

$$f^{-1}:y \mapsto y-2$$

Fig. 23.4

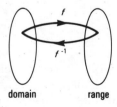

domain   range

Specimen question If $f:x \mapsto x^2$, find
(a)   the range if the domain is $\{1,4\}$;
(b)   the domain if the range is $\{1,4\}$.

Answer
(a)   When $x = 1$, $x^2 = 1$, and when $x = 4$, $x^2 = 16$, so the range is $\{1,16\}$.
(b)   When $x^2 = 1$, $x = -1$ or 1, and when $x^2 = 4$, $x = -2$ or $+2$, so that the domain is $\{-2, -1, 1, 2\}$. This is illustrated by the Papy graph in Fig. 23.5.

Fig. 23.5

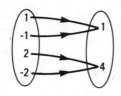

Specimen question If $f{:}x\mapsto 3x+4$, find the inverse function f^{-1}.

Answer It may help to denote the image of any element x by y. Then $y = 3x+4$, so that $x = \frac{1}{3}(y-4)$. The inverse function is such that $f^{-1}{:}y\mapsto\frac{1}{3}(y-4)$, or, in terms of x, $f{:}x\mapsto\frac{1}{3}(x-4)$.

Specimen question If $f{:}x\mapsto x^2$, find the inverse relation.

Answer The inverse relation is clearly $f^{-1}{:}y\mapsto\pm\sqrt{y}$. If the domain contains positive and negative numbers, then each element in the range is associated with two elements in the domain (Fig. 23.6(a)), and the relation is not a function. If, however, the domain only contains positive numbers (or only negative numbers) then there is no ambiguity, and the inverse relation can be described as a function (Fig. 23.6(b)).

Fig. 23.6

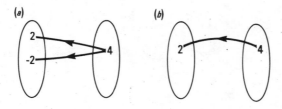

(a)   (b)

COMPOSITE FUNCTION

The function $f{:}x\mapsto 3x+2$ can be described as two separate functions. First an element x is multiplied by 3 then 2 is added. If $g{:}x\mapsto 3x$ and $h{:}x\mapsto x+2$, then $f = hg$. Notice the order. Denote the image of the element 1 under f by $f(1)$. Then from our definition of f, $f(1) = 3\times1+2$, i.e. $f(1) = 5$. But $g(1) = 3$ and $h(3) = 5$, so that $f(1) = hg(1)$, whereas $h(1) = 3$ and $g(3) = 9$, so that $f(1) \neq gh(1)$. Always read from the element: that is, from right to left. We see similarly that $(gf)^{-1} = f^{-1}g^{-1}$, as in the example following.

Specimen question If:

$$f{:}x\mapsto x+2 \text{ and } g{:}x\mapsto\frac{1}{x}$$

find the inverse functions f^{-1}, g^{-1}. Find $f(2)$, $gf(2)$ $fg(2)$, $f^{-1}g^{-1}(2)$ and $g^{-1}f^{-1}(2)$.

Answer Since

$$f:x\mapsto x+2, f^{-1}:x\mapsto x-2$$

Since

$$g:x\mapsto\frac{1}{x}, g^{-1}:x\mapsto\frac{1}{x}$$

Moreover, $f(2) = 4$, so $gf(2) = g(4) = \frac{1}{4}$, whereas $g(2) = \frac{1}{2}$ and $fg(2) = f(\frac{1}{2}) = 2\frac{1}{2}$. Also $f^{-1}g^{-1}(\frac{1}{4}) = f^{-1}(4) = 2$, but $g^{-1}f^{-1}(\frac{1}{4}) = g^{-1}(-\frac{7}{4}) = -\frac{4}{7}$.

EXAMINATION QUESTIONS 23

1   If $f:x\mapsto x+1$ and $g:x\mapsto\frac{1}{2}x$, find:
   (a) $f(1)$,
   (b) $gf(1)$,
   (c) $fg(1)$,
   (d) $f^{-1}(1)$,
   (e) $g^{-1}(1)$
   (f) $f^{-1}g^{-1}(1)$

2   If $f:x\mapsto x-3$ and $g:x\mapsto\frac{2}{x}$, find the inverse functions f^{-1}, g^{-1}. Find also the function $(fg)^{-1}$.

MATRICES

CONTENTS

▶ **Summary** 243

▶ **Definition** 243

▶ **Examples of matrices displaying information** 244

▶ **Matrix addition** 244

▶ **Multiplication** 245
Scalar multiples 245
Multiplication of matrices 245

▶ **Zero matrix, identity matrix** 246

▶ **Equal matrices** 246

▶ **Examination questions 24A** 247

▶ **Determinant of a matrix** 248

▶ **Inverse matrix** 249

▶ **Examination questions 24B** 250

SUMMARY

♦ Two matrices can only be **added** together if they have the same number of rows and columns, e.g.

$$\begin{pmatrix} a & b \\ c & d \end{pmatrix} + \begin{pmatrix} x & y \\ z & w \end{pmatrix} = \begin{pmatrix} a+x & b+y \\ c+z & d+w \end{pmatrix}$$

but:

$$\begin{pmatrix} a & b \\ c & d \end{pmatrix} \text{ and } \begin{pmatrix} x \\ z \end{pmatrix} \text{ cannot be added together.}$$

♦ The matrix **A** can only **multiply** the matrix **B** if **A** has the same number of columns as **B** has rows, e.g.

$$\begin{pmatrix} a & b \\ c & d \end{pmatrix}\begin{pmatrix} x \\ z \end{pmatrix} \text{ exists, but } \begin{pmatrix} x \\ z \end{pmatrix}\begin{pmatrix} a & b \\ c & d \end{pmatrix} \text{ does not}$$

♦ To **multiply** two matrices, each row of the first 'dives down' the corresponding row of the second:

$$\begin{pmatrix} a & b \\ c & d \end{pmatrix}\begin{pmatrix} x \\ z \end{pmatrix} = \begin{pmatrix} ax+bz \\ cx+dz \end{pmatrix}$$

NB Matrix multiplication is not commutative; in general:

A . B ≠ B . A

♦ The **inverse** of the 2×2 matrix:

$$\begin{pmatrix} a & b \\ c & d \end{pmatrix}$$

is:

$$\frac{1}{ad-bc}\begin{pmatrix} d & -b \\ -c & a \end{pmatrix}$$

DEFINITION

Matrices are arrays of numbers, which may have been set out so that they display information conveniently, and which are subject to certain laws of combination, especially addition and multiplication.

EXAMPLES OF MATRICES DISPLAYING INFORMATION

The letters posted by a small company in one week are shown in Table 24.1.

Table 24.1

	First class	Second class
Monday	12	25
Tuesday	24	35
Wednesday	28	40
Thursday	16	30
Friday	36	40

This information can be displayed in the matrix:

$$\begin{pmatrix} 12 & 25 \\ 24 & 35 \\ 28 & 40 \\ 16 & 30 \\ 36 & 40 \end{pmatrix}$$

Fig. 24.1

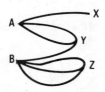

Similarly, the route matrix below described the routes in Fig. 24.1 where there is a road from town A to town X, but no road from town B to town X.

$$\begin{array}{c} \\ A \\ B \end{array}\begin{array}{ccc} X & Y & Z \\ \end{array}\begin{pmatrix} 1 & 2 & 0 \\ 0 & 1 & 3 \end{pmatrix}$$

MATRIX ADDITION

Add the corresponding elements, thus:

$$\begin{pmatrix} 2 & 1 & 3 \\ 1 & 0 & 4 \end{pmatrix} + \begin{pmatrix} 3 & -1 & -2 \\ 4 & 0 & -2 \end{pmatrix} = \begin{pmatrix} 5 & 0 & 1 \\ 5 & 0 & 2 \end{pmatrix}$$

Since we have to add corresponding elements, matrices must have the same number of rows and columns if they are to be added (or subtracted), thus:

$$\begin{pmatrix} 4 & 1 \\ 1 & 2 \end{pmatrix} \text{ cannot be added to } \begin{pmatrix} 5 \\ 2 \end{pmatrix}$$

...LTIPLICATION

...AR MULTIPLES

Twice a matrix $\mathbf{A}$ is written $2\mathbf{A}$, where we double each element in matrix $\mathbf{A}$, e.g. if:

$$\mathbf{A} = \begin{pmatrix} 2 & 0 & -1 \\ \frac{1}{2} & 0 & 4 \end{pmatrix}, \text{ then } 2\mathbf{A} = \begin{pmatrix} 4 & 0 & -2 \\ 1 & 0 & 8 \end{pmatrix}$$

Specimen question If:

$$\mathbf{A} = \begin{pmatrix} 2 & 1 \\ 4 & -1 \end{pmatrix}, \mathbf{B} = \begin{pmatrix} 1 & 0 \\ 1 & 2 \end{pmatrix} \mathbf{C} = \begin{pmatrix} 4 & 5 & 6 \\ 3 & 2 & 1 \end{pmatrix}$$

Find, if possible:
(a) $\mathbf{A}+\mathbf{B}$
(b) $\mathbf{A}+\mathbf{C}$,
(c) $3\mathbf{A}$,
(d) $\frac{1}{2}\mathbf{C}$.

Answer
(a)   Since $\mathbf{A}$ and $\mathbf{B}$ both have two rows and two columns (and so are called '2-by-2 matrices'), we can find their sum:

$$\mathbf{A}+\mathbf{B} = \begin{pmatrix} 3 & 1 \\ 5 & 1 \end{pmatrix}$$

(b)   Since $\mathbf{A}$ has two columns and $\mathbf{C}$ has three columns, we cannot add them together, so that $\mathbf{A}+\mathbf{C}$ does not exist.

(c) $3\mathbf{A} = 3\begin{pmatrix} 2 & 1 \\ 4 & -1 \end{pmatrix} = \begin{pmatrix} 6 & 3 \\ 12 & -3 \end{pmatrix}$

(d) $\frac{1}{2}\mathbf{C} = \frac{1}{2}\begin{pmatrix} 4 & 5 & 6 \\ 3 & 2 & 1 \end{pmatrix} = \begin{pmatrix} 2 & \frac{5}{2} & 3 \\ \frac{3}{2} & 1 & \frac{1}{2} \end{pmatrix}$

...TIPLICATION OF ...RICES

If:

$$\mathbf{A} = \begin{pmatrix} 1 & 2 \\ 3 & 4 \end{pmatrix} \text{ and } \mathbf{B} = \begin{pmatrix} 5 & 6 & 7 \\ 8 & 9 & 0 \end{pmatrix}$$

to find the product $\mathbf{A}.\mathbf{B}$ we let each row of $\mathbf{A}$ 'dive down' the corresponding column of $\mathbf{B}$, multiplying the associated elements and adding these products, thus:

$$\mathbf{A}.\mathbf{B} = \begin{pmatrix} 1 & 2 \\ 3 & 4 \end{pmatrix}\begin{pmatrix} 5 & 6 & 7 \\ 8 & 9 & 0 \end{pmatrix} = \begin{pmatrix} 5 \boxed{1} & 6 & 7 \\ 8 \boxed{2} & 9 & 0 \end{pmatrix}$$

to find the element in the first row and first column of $\mathbf{A}.\mathbf{B}$. This element is $1\times5+2\times8$, i.e. 21. To find the element in the first row and third column of $\mathbf{A}.\mathbf{B}$, let the first row of $\mathbf{A}$ 'dive down' the third column of $\mathbf{B}$:

$$\begin{pmatrix} 5 & 6 & 7 & \boxed{1} \\ 8 & 9 & 0 & \boxed{2} \end{pmatrix}$$

so the element in the first row, third column is $1\times7+2\times0$, i.e. 7. So we have found that:

$$\mathbf{A.B} = \begin{pmatrix} 21 & — & 7 \\ \rule{1em}{0.4pt} & \rule{1em}{0.4pt} & \rule{1em}{0.4pt} \end{pmatrix}$$

The missing entries are found in the same way, so that:

$$\mathbf{A.B} = \begin{pmatrix} 21 & 24 & 7 \\ 47 & 54 & 21 \end{pmatrix}$$

Since **B** has three columns and **A** has only two rows, we cannot find the product **B.A**, for:

$$\mathbf{B.A} = \begin{pmatrix} \boxed{5\ 6\ 7} \\ 8\ 9\ 0 \end{pmatrix}\begin{pmatrix} 1 & 2 \\ 3 & 4 \end{pmatrix} = \begin{pmatrix} 1 & \boxed{5} & 2 \\ 3 & \boxed{6} & 4 \\ ? & \boxed{7} & \end{pmatrix}$$

NB Matrix multiplication is not commutative; in general:

$$\mathbf{A.B} \neq \mathbf{B.A}$$

ZERO MATRIX, IDENTITY MATRIX

A matrix with every element zero is called a zero matrix, e.g.

$$\begin{pmatrix} 0 & 0 \\ 0 & 0 \end{pmatrix}$$

is the zero matrix of order two; a matrix with a 1 in every element the leading diagonal and a zero everywhere else is called a u matrix, e.g.

$$\begin{pmatrix} 1 & 0 \\ 0 & 1 \end{pmatrix}$$

is the unit matrix of order two.

EQUAL MATRICES

Two matrices are equal if, and only if, every element of one is equal the corresponding element of the other, thus if:

$$\begin{pmatrix} a & b \\ c & d \end{pmatrix} = \begin{pmatrix} 3 & 4 \\ 5 & 6 \end{pmatrix}, a = 3, b = 4, c = 5, d = 6$$

This often enables us to solve certain equations.

Specimen question If:

$$\begin{pmatrix} a & 3a \\ 2b & b \end{pmatrix}\begin{pmatrix} 2 \\ 3 \end{pmatrix} = \begin{pmatrix} 44 \\ 42 \end{pmatrix}$$

Find a and b.

Answer Multiplying:

$$\begin{pmatrix} a & 3a \\ 2b & b \end{pmatrix}\begin{pmatrix} 2 \\ 3 \end{pmatrix} = \begin{pmatrix} 11a \\ 7b \end{pmatrix}$$

$$\therefore \begin{pmatrix} 11a \\ 7b \end{pmatrix} = \begin{pmatrix} 44 \\ 42 \end{pmatrix}$$

$11a = 44$, $7b = 42$, so that $a = 4$ and $b = 6$.

AMINATION QUESTIONS 24A

1 If $\mathbf{A} = \begin{pmatrix} 2 & -1 \\ 4 & 3 \end{pmatrix}$, $\mathbf{B} = \begin{pmatrix} 3 & 0 \\ 5 & 1 \end{pmatrix}$, $\mathbf{C} = \begin{pmatrix} 2 \\ 3 \end{pmatrix}$, $\mathbf{D} = (2 \ -1)$,

find:

(a) $\mathbf{A+B}$	(b) $\mathbf{A-2B}$	(c) $3\mathbf{A}+2\mathbf{B}$	(d) $\mathbf{A.B}$
(e) $\mathbf{B.A}$	(f) $\mathbf{A.C}$	(g) $\mathbf{B.C}$	(h) $\mathbf{D.A}$
(i) $\mathbf{D.B}$	(j) $\mathbf{C.D}$	(k) $\mathbf{D.C}$	(l) $\mathbf{A^2}$

What happens when we try to find $\mathbf{A.D}$?

2 If $\begin{pmatrix} 1 & -3 \\ 4 & x \end{pmatrix}\begin{pmatrix} y \\ 5 \end{pmatrix} = \begin{pmatrix} 1 \\ 4 \end{pmatrix}$ find the values of x and y.

3 If $\begin{pmatrix} 0 & 4 \\ 3 & -1 \end{pmatrix}\begin{pmatrix} a \\ b \end{pmatrix} = \begin{pmatrix} -12 \\ a \end{pmatrix}$ find the values of a and b.

4 Multiply each side of the matrix equation:

$$\begin{pmatrix} 5 & 2 \\ 3 & 1 \end{pmatrix}\begin{pmatrix} x \\ y \end{pmatrix} = \begin{pmatrix} 4 \\ 4 \end{pmatrix}$$

by the matrix $\begin{pmatrix} 1 & -2 \\ -3 & 5 \end{pmatrix}$ and so find x and y.

5 If $\mathbf{A} = \begin{pmatrix} 0 & -1 \\ 1 & 0 \end{pmatrix}$, find $\mathbf{A}^2$ and $\mathbf{A}^3$, and show that $\mathbf{A}^4$ is the two-by-two unit matrix.

6 Let $\mathbf{A}$ be the matrix of letters posted on p.244. If it costs 18p to send a letter first class and 13p to send a letter second class, let $\mathbf{B} = \begin{pmatrix} 18 \\ 13 \end{pmatrix}$. Form the matrix product $\mathbf{A.B}$, and interpret your answer. Let $\mathbf{C} = (1 \ 1 \ 1 \ 1 \ 1)$. Form the matrix products $\mathbf{C.A}$, $\mathbf{C.(A.B)}$, and interpret each answer.

7 Let $\mathbf{A}$ be the route matrix on page 244. Let $\mathbf{B}$ be the route matrix that describes the routes between X, Y and Z and P, Q, R and S in Fig. 24.2. Write down the matrix $\mathbf{B}$ and find the product $\mathbf{A.B}$. What is the interpretation of the element in the first row and third column?

8 In 1880, England beat Wales at rugby football, scoring seven goals, one dropped goal and six tries, while Wales failed to score. Display

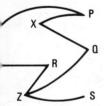

24.2

this information in a matrix **A** with two rows and three colum
Taking the later scoring values of 5 points for a goal, 4 for a drop
goal and 3 for a try, form a matrix **B** such that the product **A.B** gi
the scores of each team in this match. Form another matrix **C** givi
the scores of 6 points for a goal, 4 for a try and 3 for a dropped goal,
that the product **A.C** gives the scores for the match.

9   (i) Write down the matrix **M** which is the route matrix for
network shown in Fig. 24.3:

Fig. 24.3

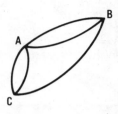

(ii) Calculate the matrix $\mathbf{M}^2$.
(iii) Write down the number of two-stage routes from A to C
[LEAG specimen question]

DETERMINANT OF A MATRIX

The determinant of the 2×2 matrix:

$\begin{pmatrix} a & b \\ c & d \end{pmatrix}$ is $ad - bc$

e.g. the determinant of:

$\begin{pmatrix} 3 & 1 \\ 2 & 5 \end{pmatrix}$ is $3 \times 5 - 2 \times 1 = 13$

and of:

$\begin{pmatrix} 3 & -1 \\ 2 & 4 \end{pmatrix}$ is $3 \times 4 - 2 \times (-1) = 14$.

A matrix whose determinant is zero, e.g.

$\begin{pmatrix} 2 & 4 \\ 1 & 2 \end{pmatrix}$

is called a **singular** matrix.

INVERSE MATRIX

The inverse of a matrix **A** (written $\mathbf{A}^{-1}$) is the matrix such that $\mathbf{A}.\mathbf{A}^{-1} = \mathbf{A}^{-1}.\mathbf{A} = \mathbf{I}$, where **I** is the appropriate unit matrix.

$$\begin{pmatrix} 5 & 3 \\ -2 & -1 \end{pmatrix}\begin{pmatrix} -1 & -3 \\ 2 & 5 \end{pmatrix} = \begin{pmatrix} -1 & -3 \\ 2 & 5 \end{pmatrix}\begin{pmatrix} 5 & 3 \\ -2 & -1 \end{pmatrix} = \begin{pmatrix} 1 & 0 \\ 0 & 1 \end{pmatrix}$$

so that:

$$\begin{pmatrix} -1 & -3 \\ 2 & 5 \end{pmatrix} \text{ is the inverse of } \begin{pmatrix} 5 & 3 \\ -2 & -1 \end{pmatrix}$$

and also:

$$\begin{pmatrix} 5 & 3 \\ -2 & -1 \end{pmatrix} \text{ is the inverse of } \begin{pmatrix} -1 & -3 \\ 2 & 5 \end{pmatrix}$$

In general, to find the inverse of the matrix

$$\begin{pmatrix} a & b \\ c & d \end{pmatrix}$$

interchange the two elements in the leading diagonal

$$\begin{pmatrix} d & \\ & a \end{pmatrix}$$

and change the sign of the other two

$$\begin{pmatrix} d & -b \\ -c & a \end{pmatrix}$$

then divide by the value of the determinant $(ad-bc)$, so the inverse is

$$\frac{1}{ad-bc}\begin{pmatrix} d & -b \\ -c & a \end{pmatrix}$$

NB In the matrix

$$\begin{pmatrix} 5 & 3 \\ -2 & -1 \end{pmatrix}$$

the determinant is 1 so that we have only to interchange 5 and -1 then change the signs of the other elements.

Specimen question Find the inverse of:

$$\begin{pmatrix} 6 & 3 \\ 3 & 4 \end{pmatrix}$$

Answer Interchange the elements in the leading diagonal:

$$\begin{pmatrix} 4 & \\ & 6 \end{pmatrix}$$

Change the signs of the other two:

$$\begin{pmatrix} 4 & -3 \\ -3 & 6 \end{pmatrix}$$

Divide by the value of the determinant, $6\times4-3\times3$, i.e. 15, so t
inverse is

$$\frac{1}{15}\begin{pmatrix} 4 & -3 \\ -3 & 6 \end{pmatrix}$$

EXAMINATION QUESTIONS 24B

1　Find the value of the determinant of each of the following matrices:

　　(a) $\begin{pmatrix} 2 & 5 \\ 1 & 4 \end{pmatrix}$　　　(b) $\begin{pmatrix} 2 & 5 \\ -1 & 4 \end{pmatrix}$　　　(c) $\begin{pmatrix} 3 & 4 \\ 2 & 3 \end{pmatrix}$　　　(d) $\begin{pmatrix} 3 & 1 \\ 1 & 0 \end{pmatrix}$

2　Which of the following matrices is singular?

　　(a) $\begin{pmatrix} 2 & 4 \\ \frac{1}{2} & 1 \end{pmatrix}$　　　(b) $\begin{pmatrix} 2 & 1 \\ 0 & 0 \end{pmatrix}$　　　(c) $\begin{pmatrix} 0 & 1 \\ 1 & 0 \end{pmatrix}$　　　(d) $\begin{pmatrix} 1 & 1 \\ -1 & 1 \end{pmatrix}$

3　Find the inverse of each of the following matrices:

　　(a) $\begin{pmatrix} 2 & 1 \\ 4 & 3 \end{pmatrix}$　　　(b) $\begin{pmatrix} 3 & 1 \\ 5 & 2 \end{pmatrix}$　　　(c) $\begin{pmatrix} 3 & -1 \\ 5 & 2 \end{pmatrix}$

　　(d) $\begin{pmatrix} 2 & 4 \\ -\frac{1}{2} & 2 \end{pmatrix}$　　　(e) $\begin{pmatrix} 2 & 0 \\ 0 & 2 \end{pmatrix}$　　　(f) $\begin{pmatrix} 2 & 1 \\ 1 & 0 \end{pmatrix}$

4　If $\mathbf{M} = \begin{pmatrix} 3 & 2 \\ -1 & 2 \end{pmatrix}$, find $\mathbf{M}^{-1}$. Hence find x and y if:

$$\mathbf{M}\begin{pmatrix} x \\ y \end{pmatrix} = \begin{pmatrix} 13 \\ 1 \end{pmatrix}$$

5　If $\mathbf{M} = \begin{pmatrix} 3 & -2 \\ 1 & 1 \end{pmatrix}$, find x and y when:

$$\mathbf{M}\begin{pmatrix} x \\ y \end{pmatrix} = \begin{pmatrix} 1 \\ 1 \end{pmatrix}$$

6　If $\mathbf{M} = \begin{pmatrix} 4 & 2 \\ 1 & 3 \end{pmatrix}$, $\mathbf{x} = \begin{pmatrix} x \\ y \end{pmatrix}$ and $\mathbf{M.x} = \mathbf{p}$, find x and y when $\mathbf{p} =$

　　(a) $\begin{pmatrix} 10 \\ -1 \end{pmatrix}$　　　(b) $\begin{pmatrix} 2 \\ 4 \end{pmatrix}$　　　(c) $\begin{pmatrix} 1 \\ 0 \end{pmatrix}$

7　The simultaneous equations $3x+4y = 2$, $x+2y = 0$ may be written
matrix form:

$$\begin{pmatrix} 3 & 4 \\ 1 & 2 \end{pmatrix}\begin{pmatrix} x \\ y \end{pmatrix} = \begin{pmatrix} 2 \\ 0 \end{pmatrix}$$

Find the inverse of the matrix $\begin{pmatrix} 3 & 4 \\ 1 & 2 \end{pmatrix}$ to solve the following pairs
simultaneous equations for x and y.

8 Use a matrix method to solve the following pairs of simultaneous equations:

(a) $2x+3y = 1, \quad x+5y = -3$

(b) $2x+3y = -2, \, x+5y = -3$

(c) $2x+3y = 1, \quad x+5y = 1$

GEOMETRICAL APPLICATIONS OF MATRICES

CONTENTS

▶ Summary 255

▶ Mappings 256

▶ Reflection 257

▶ Rotation 258

▶ Enlargement 259

▶ Shear 259

▶ Mapping of a singular matrix 260

▶ Change of area 260

▶ Examination questions 25 261

SUMMARY

♦ **Enlargement factor k**

Fig. 25.1(a)

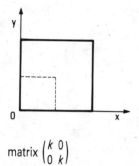

matrix $\begin{pmatrix} k & 0 \\ 0 & k \end{pmatrix}$

♦ **Reflection in x-axis**

Fig. 25.1(b)

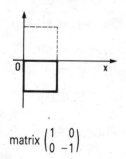

matrix $\begin{pmatrix} 1 & 0 \\ 0 & -1 \end{pmatrix}$

♦ **Reflection in y-axis**

Fig. 25.1(c)

matrix $\begin{pmatrix} -1 & 0 \\ 0 & 1 \end{pmatrix}$

♦ **Rotation through an angle α**

Fig. 25.1(*d*)

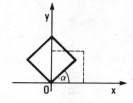

matrix $\begin{pmatrix} \cos\alpha & -\sin\alpha \\ \sin\alpha & \cos\alpha \end{pmatrix}$

♦ **Shear parallel to *x*-axis**

Fig. 25.1(*e*)

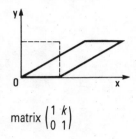

matrix $\begin{pmatrix} 1 & k \\ 0 & 1 \end{pmatrix}$

MAPPINGS

Since matrices can be used to display information, a matrix can give the coordinates of a point, $\begin{pmatrix} x \\ y \end{pmatrix}$ or sometimes $(x\ y)$, in two dimensions, or all the vertices of a polygon. For example:

$$\begin{pmatrix} 0 & 1 & 1 & 0 \\ 0 & 0 & 1 & 1 \end{pmatrix}$$

represents the unit square shown in Fig. 25.2

Fig. 25.2

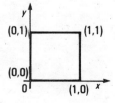

Multiplication by a matrix maps the unit square into another figure, e.g. since:

$$\begin{pmatrix} 3 & 2 \\ -1 & 1 \end{pmatrix}\begin{pmatrix} 0 & 1 & 1 & 0 \\ 0 & 0 & 1 & 1 \end{pmatrix} = \begin{pmatrix} 0 & 3 & 5 & 2 \\ 0 & -1 & 0 & 1 \end{pmatrix}$$

the matrix

$$\begin{pmatrix} 3 & 2 \\ -1 & 1 \end{pmatrix}$$

transforms the unit square into the parallelogram OPQR (Fig. 25.3). It is often easy to describe by a matrix a transformation that would be almost impossible to describe by words.

Fig. 25.3

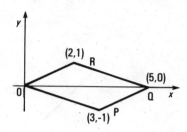

REFLECTION

Since

$$\begin{pmatrix} 1 & 0 \\ 0 & -1 \end{pmatrix}\begin{pmatrix} x \\ y \end{pmatrix} = \begin{pmatrix} x \\ -y \end{pmatrix}$$

the matrix

$$\begin{pmatrix} 1 & 0 \\ 0 & -1 \end{pmatrix}$$

describes a reflection in the x-axis (Fig. 25.4(a)). Similarly

$$\begin{pmatrix} -1 & 0 \\ 0 & 1 \end{pmatrix}$$

describes a reflection in the y-axis (Fig. 25.4(b)).

Fig. 25.4

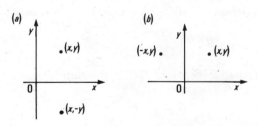

Since

$$\begin{pmatrix} 0 & 1 \\ 1 & 0 \end{pmatrix}\begin{pmatrix} x \\ y \end{pmatrix} = \begin{pmatrix} y \\ x \end{pmatrix}$$

the matrix

$$\begin{pmatrix} 0 & 1 \\ 1 & 0 \end{pmatrix}$$

describes a reflection in the line $y = x$, and similarly

$$\begin{pmatrix} 0 & -1 \\ -1 & 0 \end{pmatrix}$$

describes reflection in the line $y = -x$ (Fig. 25.5(a) and (b)).

Fig. 25.5

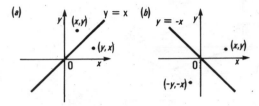

ROTATION

Since

$$\begin{pmatrix} 0 & 1 \\ -1 & 0 \end{pmatrix}\begin{pmatrix} x \\ y \end{pmatrix} = \begin{pmatrix} y \\ -x \end{pmatrix}$$

the matrix

$$\mathbf{R} = \begin{pmatrix} 0 & 1 \\ -1 & 0 \end{pmatrix}$$

represents a rotation through 90° in a clockwise sense (Fig. 25.6). The matrix

$$\mathbf{R}^2 = \begin{pmatrix} -1 & 0 \\ 0 & -1 \end{pmatrix}$$

represents a rotation through 180° in a clockwise sense, and

$$\mathbf{R}^3 = \begin{pmatrix} 0 & -1 \\ 1 & 0 \end{pmatrix}$$

a rotation through 270° in the same sense.

Fig. 25.6

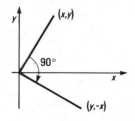

ENLARGEMENT

Since

$$\begin{pmatrix} k & 0 \\ 0 & 1 \end{pmatrix} \begin{pmatrix} x \\ y \end{pmatrix} = \begin{pmatrix} kx \\ y \end{pmatrix}$$

this matrix describes a stretching parallel to the x-axis (Fig. 25.7(a)), and

$$\begin{pmatrix} 1 & 0 \\ 0 & k \end{pmatrix}$$

a stretching parallel to the y-axis (Fig. 25.7(b)).

Fig. 25.7

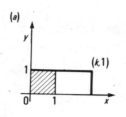 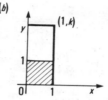

The matrix

$$\begin{pmatrix} k & 0 \\ 0 & k \end{pmatrix}$$

describes an enlargement, centre (0,0), factor k (Fig. 25.8).

Fig. 25.8

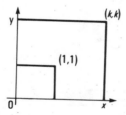

SHEAR

Since

$$\begin{pmatrix} 1 & k \\ 0 & 1 \end{pmatrix}\begin{pmatrix} 0 & 1 & 1 & 0 \\ 0 & 0 & 1 & 1 \end{pmatrix} = \begin{pmatrix} 0 & 1 & 1+k & k \\ 0 & 0 & 1 & 1 \end{pmatrix}$$

the matrix

$$\begin{pmatrix} 1 & k \\ 0 & 1 \end{pmatrix}$$

maps the unit square into a paralellogram (Fig. 25.9); such a transformation is called a shear parallel to the x-axis. Similarly

$$\begin{pmatrix} 1 & 0 \\ k & 1 \end{pmatrix}$$

describes a shear parallel to the y-axis.

Fig. 25.9

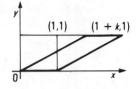

MAPPING OF A SINGULAR MATRIX

Any singular matrix can be written

$$\begin{pmatrix} a & b \\ ka & kb \end{pmatrix}$$

and maps the unit square into $(0, 0)$, (a, ka), (b, kb), $(a+b, ka+kb)$. These points lie on the straight line whose equation is $y = kx$, and the matrix maps the unit square into a line-segment (Fig. 25.10).

Fig. 25.10

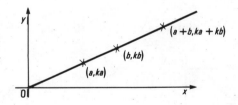

CHANGE OF AREA

It can be shown that the ratio of the area of the transformed region to that of the original is always $D:1$, where D is the value of the determinant of the matrix that describes the transformation. Notice that the determinant of a singular matrix is zero, and the area of the line-segment on to which it maps the unit square is obviously zero.

Specimen question Plot the points whose vertices are described by the matrix:

$$\begin{pmatrix} 0 & 2 & 2 & 0 \\ 0 & 0 & 2 & 2 \end{pmatrix}$$

Find the figure into which OABC is mapped by the matrix

$$\begin{pmatrix} 1 & 1 \\ -1 & 1 \end{pmatrix}$$

Describe the transformation, and find the ratio of the area of the figure OABC to that of the transformed figure OA'B'C'.

Fig. 25.11

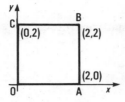

Answer The points whose coordinates are given by the matrix are plotted in Fig. 25.11. Since:

$$\begin{pmatrix} 1 & 1 \\ -1 & 1 \end{pmatrix}\begin{pmatrix} 0 & 2 & 2 & 0 \\ 0 & 0 & 2 & 2 \end{pmatrix} = \begin{pmatrix} 0 & 2 & 4 & 2 \\ 0 & -2 & 0 & 2 \end{pmatrix}$$

Fig. 25.12 shows both OABC and the transformed figure. The transformation is a rotation in a clockwise sense through 45° and an enlargement centre (0, 0), factor $\sqrt{2}$.

Since all lengths are enlarged by a factor $\sqrt{2}$, the area is enlarged by a factor 2, so the ratio of the old area to the new is 1:2. Notice also that the determinant of

$$\begin{pmatrix} 1 & -1 \\ 1 & 1 \end{pmatrix}$$

is 2.

Fig. 25.12

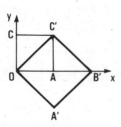

1 Which of the following matrices represents:
   (a)   a rotation about the origin of 90° in a clockwise sense;
   (b)   a rotation about the origin of 90° in an anti-clockwise sense?

   (i) $\begin{pmatrix} 1 & 0 \\ 0 & -1 \end{pmatrix}$

   (ii) $\begin{pmatrix} 0 & -1 \\ 1 & 0 \end{pmatrix}$

   (iii) $\begin{pmatrix} 0 & -1 \\ -1 & 0 \end{pmatrix}$

(iv) $\begin{pmatrix} -1 & 0 \\ 0 & 1 \end{pmatrix}$

(v) $\begin{pmatrix} 0 & 1 \\ -1 & 0 \end{pmatrix}$

2   Which of the following matrices represents an enlargement, centre (0, 0), scale factor 4?

(i) $\begin{pmatrix} 2 & 0 \\ 0 & 2 \end{pmatrix}$

(ii) $\begin{pmatrix} 4 & 0 \\ 0 & 4 \end{pmatrix}$

(iii) $\begin{pmatrix} 4 & 0 \\ 0 & 1 \end{pmatrix}$

(iv) $\begin{pmatrix} 4 & 0 \\ 0 & -4 \end{pmatrix}$

(v) $\begin{pmatrix} 2 & 0 \\ 0 & -2 \end{pmatrix}$

3   If $S = \begin{pmatrix} 1 & 0 \\ 3 & 1 \end{pmatrix}$

find the transformation made by **S** on the unit square.

If $R = \begin{pmatrix} 0 & -1 \\ -1 & 0 \end{pmatrix}$

find the matrix **T** given by **RSR** and describe the transformation it represents.

4   The vertices of a square side 5 units are given by the matrix:

$$\begin{pmatrix} 0 & 5 & 5 & 0 \\ 0 & 0 & 5 & 5 \end{pmatrix}$$

Find the transformation made on this square by the matrix

$$\begin{pmatrix} 0.6 & 0.8 \\ -0.8 & 0.6 \end{pmatrix}$$

by drawing the original square and the figure into which it is trans formed, and using geometrical instruments to make any necessary measurements.

5   On graph paper mark the points whose coordinates are given by the matrix **T**, where:

$$T = \begin{pmatrix} 1 & 3 & 5 \\ 1 & 2 & 2 \end{pmatrix}$$

Join the points to form a triangle T. The triangle T is transformed into a triangle U by means of the matrix

$$P = \begin{pmatrix} 0 & 1 \\ -1 & 0 \end{pmatrix}$$

and T is also transformed into the triangle V by the matrix

$$Q = \begin{pmatrix} 1 & 1 \\ 0 & 1 \end{pmatrix}$$

Mark these triangles on the graph paper and describe the geometrical transformations as precisely as possible.

On another sheet of graph paper, draw the triangle T again, and find the transformations represented by the matrices P^{-1} and Q^{-1}.

VECTORS

CONTENTS

▶ Summary   267

▶ Definition   268

▶ Displacement vectors   268

▶ Addition of vectors   269

▶ Addition of components   269

▶ Subtraction of vectors   270

▶ Magnitude of a vector   270

▶ Direction   270

▶ Parallel and perpendicular vectors   271

▶ Examination questions 26A   272

▶ Use of geometry   272

▶ Examination questions 26B   273

▶ **Geometrical applications** 274

The diagonals of a parallelogram bisect each other 274

▶ **Examination questions 26C** 275

- **Vectors** are physical quantities having magnitude and direction, combined according to certain laws. Examples of vectors are displacement, velocity, acceleration, force and momentum.

- **Scalar** quantities can be described by a number alone. Examples of scalars are length, area, time, mass, temperature.

- A vector in two dimensions, components x and y, can be represented by $x\mathbf{i}+y\mathbf{j}$ or by a column matrix

$$\begin{pmatrix} x \\ y \end{pmatrix}$$

or sometimes by a row matrix $(x\ y)$. The magnitude of this vector is:

$$\sqrt{x^2+y^2}$$

- We **add** vectors by completing a parallelogram as shown in Fig. 26.1. This is equivalent to adding the components, e.g.

$$\begin{pmatrix} a \\ b \end{pmatrix} + \begin{pmatrix} c \\ d \end{pmatrix} = \begin{pmatrix} a+c \\ b+d \end{pmatrix}$$

Fig. 26.1

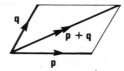

- To subtract $\mathbf{q}$ from $\mathbf{p}$, we add $-\mathbf{q}$ to $\mathbf{p}$ (Fig. 26.2). This is equivalent to subtracting the components, e.g.

$$\begin{pmatrix} a \\ b \end{pmatrix} - \begin{pmatrix} c \\ d \end{pmatrix} = \begin{pmatrix} a-c \\ b-d \end{pmatrix}$$

Fig. 26.2

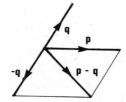

• If points A, B have position vectors **a**, **b** relative to an origin O, the vector $\overrightarrow{AB}$ = **b**−**a** (Fig. 26.3(*a*)).

• The position vector of the mid-point M of AB relative to O is $\frac{1}{2}$(**a**+**b**) (Fig. 26.3(*b*)).

Fig. 26.3

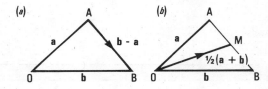

DEFINITION

A vector can be defined as a physical quantity having magnitude and direction, and subject to certain laws of composition. The only law that we define at present is addition.

DISPLACEMENT VECTORS

The simplest vectors to consider are displacement vectors, describing the position of one point relative to another. If we start at an origin O, we can travel 4 units in one direction then 3 units at right angles to the first direction, as in Fig. 26.4, and arrive at a point P. We can denote the vector that describes the displacement of P from O by $\overrightarrow{OP}$, or by a single letter, say **p**. The displacements 4 and 3 along each of the axes we call the components of **p** along Ox and Oy, and we can write them in terms of unit vectors **i** and **j** along Ox and Oy respectively, or as entries in a column matrix, or, occasionally, as entries in a row matrix, i.e.

$$\overrightarrow{OP} = \mathbf{p} = 4\mathbf{i}+3\mathbf{j} = \begin{pmatrix} 4 \\ 3 \end{pmatrix} = (4 \ \ 3)$$

The last form is easily confused with coordinates, and should be avoided.

Fig. 26.4

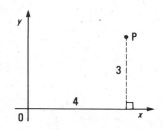

ADDITION OF VECTORS

Two vectors are added by the parallelogram law, i.e. if $\overrightarrow{OA}$ and $\overrightarrow{OB}$ are two vectors acting through a point O, then their sum $\overrightarrow{OA}+\overrightarrow{OB}$ is a vector $\overrightarrow{OC}$, also through O, where OC is the diagonal through O of the parallelogram, two of whose sides are OA and OB (Fig. 26.5). The parallelogram law of addition is the same as that sometimes described as the triangle law, but is much safer; it avoids the danger of thinking that $\overrightarrow{OA}+\overrightarrow{OB} = \overrightarrow{AB}$, using the third side of the triangle (Fig. 26.6).

Fig. 26.5

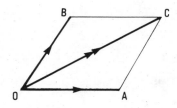

Fig. 26.6

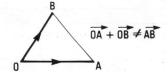

ADDITION OF COMPONENTS

If two vectors are given in terms of their components, say

$$\begin{pmatrix} a \\ b \end{pmatrix} \text{ and } \begin{pmatrix} c \\ d \end{pmatrix}$$

then we can define the sum of the vectors by

$$\begin{pmatrix} a \\ b \end{pmatrix} + \begin{pmatrix} c \\ d \end{pmatrix} = \begin{pmatrix} a+c \\ b+d \end{pmatrix}$$

This definition can be extended to three (or more) dimensions. Fig. 26.7 shows that for two dimensions the two definitions, addition using the parallelogram rule and addition of components are the same.

Fig. 26.7

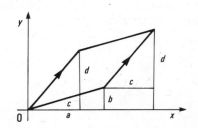

SUBTRACTION OF VECTORS

Subtraction of two vectors follows from our rule for addition, for:

$$\overrightarrow{OA}-\overrightarrow{OB} = \overrightarrow{OA}+(-\overrightarrow{OB})$$

as illustrated in Fig. 26.8. Again, if vectors are given in terms of their components, we subtract the components, e.g.

$$\binom{a}{b} - \binom{c}{d} = \binom{a-c}{b-d}$$

Fig 26.8

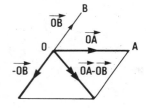

MAGNITUDE OF A VECTOR

If a vector is given in terms of its components:

$$x\mathbf{i}+y\mathbf{j} \text{ or } \binom{x}{y}$$

then the magnitude of the vector, written $|x\mathbf{i}+y\mathbf{j}|$, is $\sqrt{(x^2+y^2)}$. Thus in Fig. 26.4, the magnitude of the vector

$$4\mathbf{i}+3\mathbf{j} = \sqrt{4^2+3^2} = 5$$

which is the length of the line OP.

DIRECTION

The direction of a vector OP is usually the angle made by the vector with the positive x-axis (Fig. 26.9). If x and y are both positive, the vector $x\mathbf{i}+y\mathbf{j}$ makes with the x-axis an angle whose tangent is:

$$\left(\frac{y}{x}\right) = \tan^{-1}\left(\frac{y}{x}\right)$$

If either x or y or both is negative, it is best to draw a diagram and determine the angle from the diagram.

Fig. 26.9

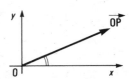

PARALLEL AND PERPENDICULAR VECTORS

If two vectors $a\mathbf{i}+b\mathbf{j}$ and $x\mathbf{i}+y\mathbf{j}$ which of course can be written:

$$\binom{a}{b}, \binom{x}{y}$$

are parallel, then

$$\frac{a}{b}=\frac{x}{y}, \text{ i.e. } ay=bx$$

If the two vectors are perpendicular, $ax+by=0$. These two results can be obtained by drawing diagrams and finding the tangents of angles that are equal.

Examples Note the following results.

1   $\binom{2}{4}+\binom{3}{1}=\binom{5}{5}$ and $\binom{2}{4}-\binom{3}{1}=\binom{-1}{3}$

This can also be written

$$(2\mathbf{i}+4\mathbf{j}) + (3\mathbf{i}+\mathbf{j}) = 5\mathbf{i}+5\mathbf{j}$$

and:

$$(2\mathbf{i}+4\mathbf{j}) - (3\mathbf{i}+\mathbf{j}) = -\mathbf{i}+3\mathbf{j}$$

2   $2\binom{2}{3}=\binom{4}{6}$ and $\frac{1}{2}\binom{2}{3}=\binom{1}{1\frac{1}{2}}$

3   The magnitude of the vector $\binom{2}{3}$ is $\sqrt{2^2+3^2}$, i.e. $\sqrt{13}$ (Fig. 26.10). The angle it makes with the x-axis is $\tan^{-1}(3/2)$

Fig. 26.10

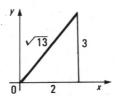

4   If the vectors $\binom{2}{3}$ and $\binom{k}{6}$ are parallel, then

$$\frac{2}{3}=\frac{k}{6}, \text{ so } k=4$$

5   If the vectors $\binom{2}{3}$ and $\binom{k}{6}$ are perpendicular then $2k+3\times6=0$, i.e. $k=-9$. The vector perpendicular to $\binom{2}{3}$ is $\binom{-9}{6}$.

1. On graph paper, draw a pair of coordinate axes. Mark the points whose coordinates are O $(0, 0)$, A $(2, 3)$, B $(3, 5)$ and C $(4, 2)$. Write down the position vectors of:
   - (a) A relative to O, i.e. $\overrightarrow{OA}$;
   - (b) B relative to O, i.e. $\overrightarrow{OB}$;
   - (c) A relative to B, i.e. $\overrightarrow{BA}$;
   - (d) B relative to A, i.e. $\overrightarrow{AB}$;
   - (e) C relative to B, i.e. $\overrightarrow{BC}$

2. Find the magnitude of each of the following vectors, and the angle it makes with the positive x-axis.
   - (a) $\begin{pmatrix} 2 \\ 2 \end{pmatrix}$
   - (b) $\begin{pmatrix} 3 \\ -3 \end{pmatrix}$
   - (c) $\begin{pmatrix} -1 \\ 1 \end{pmatrix}$
   - (d) $\begin{pmatrix} -2 \\ -2 \end{pmatrix}$

3. If $\mathbf{a} = \begin{pmatrix} 2 \\ -1 \end{pmatrix}$, $\mathbf{b} = \begin{pmatrix} 3 \\ 2 \end{pmatrix}$ and $\mathbf{c} = \begin{pmatrix} 4 \\ 0 \end{pmatrix}$, find the magnitude of:
   - (a) $\mathbf{a} + \mathbf{b}$
   - (b) $\mathbf{a} - \mathbf{c}$
   - (c) $\mathbf{a} + 2\mathbf{b}$
   - (d) $2\mathbf{a} - \mathbf{c}$
   - (e) $\mathbf{a} + \mathbf{b} + \mathbf{c}$

4. If $\begin{pmatrix} a \\ 3 \end{pmatrix}$ is parallel to $\begin{pmatrix} -1 \\ -6 \end{pmatrix}$, find a.

5. If $\begin{pmatrix} a \\ 3 \end{pmatrix}$ is perpendicular to $\begin{pmatrix} 6 \\ 1 \end{pmatrix}$, find a.

6. If $\mathbf{a} = \begin{pmatrix} 3 \\ 1 \end{pmatrix}$ and $\mathbf{b} = \begin{pmatrix} -1 \\ 2 \end{pmatrix}$, find in terms of m and n, the vector $m\mathbf{a} + n\mathbf{b}$. Hence find m and n if $m\mathbf{a} + n\mathbf{b} = \begin{pmatrix} 8 \\ 19 \end{pmatrix}$.

USE OF GEOMETRY

In all these examples, we have used the **components** of the vector. If we are given the vectors in terms of their magnitudes and directions made with a fixed line or with each other, we have to use geometry, and either scale drawing or trigonometry to find resultants, etc.

Specimen question If **u** and **v** are unit vectors inclined at 20°, find the magnitude of **u**+**v**, and the direction it makes with the vector **u**.

Fig. 26.11

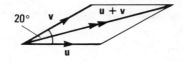

Answer Fig. 26.11 shows the parallelogram that enables us to see the vector **u**+**v**. Since the parallelogram is a rhombus, $|\mathbf{u}+\mathbf{v}| = 2 \cos 10°$ = 1.97. The angle it makes with the vector **u** is clearly 10°.

Specimen question If **u** and **v** are unit vectors inclined at 40°, find the magnitude of **u**−2**v**, and the angle it makes with the vector **u**.

Answer We can solve this problem by making a scale drawing, as in Fig. 26.12, from which we can read that $|\mathbf{u}-2\mathbf{v}|$ is 1.4, and the angle it makes with **u** is 112°. To solve the problem by calculation, it is necessary to use the cosine formula and then the sine formula, beginning:

$$x^2 = 1^2+2^2-2\times1\times2 \cos 40°$$

where $x = |\mathbf{u}-2\mathbf{v}|$.

Fig. 26.12

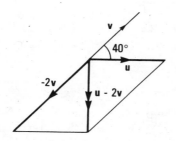

---

1 The angle between two unit vectors **p** and **q** is 60°. Calculate (*a*) $|\mathbf{p}-\mathbf{q}|$, (*b*) $|\mathbf{p}+\mathbf{q}|$.

2 The angle between two unit vectors **p** and **q** is 30°. Calculate the angle made with **p** by (*a*) **p**−**q**, (*b*) **p**+**q**.

3 Two unit vectors **u** and **v** are inclined at 50°. Find $|\mathbf{u}+\mathbf{v}|$ and the angle made by **u**+**v** with the vector **u**.

4 If **u** and **v** are unit vectors, find the angle between them if $|\mathbf{u}-\mathbf{v}| = 1.6$.

5 If **u** and **v** are unit vectors inclined at 60°, find (*a*) $|\mathbf{u}+2\mathbf{v}|$, (*b*) the angle between **u**+2**v** and the vector **u**.

GEOMETRICAL APPLICATIONS

With the usual notation, we see in Fig. 26.13 that if $\overrightarrow{OB} = \overrightarrow{OA} + \overrightarrow{AB}$, $\overrightarrow{AB} = \overrightarrow{OB} - \overrightarrow{OA}$, i.e. $\overrightarrow{AB} = b - a$, where $\overrightarrow{OB} = b$, $\overrightarrow{OA} - a$.

Fig. 26.13

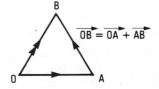

**THE DIAGONALS OF A
PARALLELOGRAM BISECT
EACH OTHER**

Let points A, B have position vectors **a** and **b** relative to O. Then the position of vector of C, the fourth vertex of the parallelogram, OACB (Fig. 26.14) is **a**+**b** and the position vector of the mid-point of OC is $\frac{1}{2}(\mathbf{a}+\mathbf{b})$. The vector describing the displacement AB is (**b**−**a**), and so the vector describing half that displacement is $\frac{1}{2}(\mathbf{b}-\mathbf{a})$; thus the position vector relative to O of the mid-point of BA is $\mathbf{a}+\frac{1}{2}(\mathbf{b}-\mathbf{a})$, i.e. $\frac{1}{2}(\mathbf{b}+\mathbf{a})$. Since the mid-points of the two diagonals have the same position vectors relative to the origin O, they must be the same points, i.e. the diagonals of a parallelogram bisect each other.

Fig. 26.14

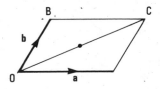

Specimen question If the position vectors of points A, B and C relative to an origin O are (1, 2), (3, 1) and (5, 3) respectively, find the fourth vertex of the parallelogram ABCD (Fig. 26.15).

Fig. 26.15

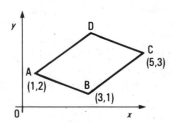

Answer The displacement vector $\overrightarrow{AD}$ must be equal to the displacement vector $\overrightarrow{BC}$. But:

$$\vec{BC} = \begin{pmatrix} 5 \\ 3 \end{pmatrix} - \begin{pmatrix} 3 \\ 1 \end{pmatrix} = \begin{pmatrix} 2 \\ 2 \end{pmatrix}$$

$$\therefore \vec{AD} = \begin{pmatrix} 2 \\ 2 \end{pmatrix}$$

But

$$\vec{OD} = \vec{OA} + \vec{AD} = \begin{pmatrix} 1 \\ 2 \end{pmatrix} + \begin{pmatrix} 2 \\ 2 \end{pmatrix} = \begin{pmatrix} 3 \\ 4 \end{pmatrix}$$

Therefore the coordinates of the fourth vertex of the parallelogram ABCD are (3, 4). Notice that if we had required the fourth vertex of the parallelogram ABDC, it is (7, 2). We must take care to draw the correct figure in these questions.

EXAMINATION QUESTIONS 26C

1   If the position vectors of points A and B relative to an origin O are **a** and **b**, write down the vector $\vec{BA}$. Write down the position vectors of X and Y, the mid-points of OA and OB. Find the vector $\vec{YX}$. Deduce a relation between the lengths of AB and XY, and the directions of AB and XY.

2   With the data of question **1**, P and Q are points on OA and OB such that OP = $\frac{1}{3}$OA, OQ = $\frac{1}{3}$OB. Use the method of question **1** to find PQ:AB.

3   If the position vectors relative to an origin O of points A, B and C are **a**, **b** and **c** respectively, find the position vector of A', the mid-point of BC, and the position vector of the point L in AA' such that AL = $\frac{2}{3}$AA'. If B' is the mid-point of AC, and M is the mid-point in BB' such that BM = $\frac{2}{3}$BB', find the position vector of M. The point N is defined in a similar way. Deduce that the medians of a triangle intersect in a point.

4   If the position vectors of points A, B and C are

$$\begin{pmatrix} 1 \\ 5 \end{pmatrix}, \begin{pmatrix} 3 \\ 1 \end{pmatrix}, \begin{pmatrix} 7 \\ 3 \end{pmatrix}$$

respectively, find the fourth vertex of the parallelogram ABCD. Use Pythagoras' theorem to prove that this parallelogram is a square.

5   In the parallelogram OABC, the line OA is produced to D so that A is the mid-point of OD. The point E on OC is such that OE = 2OC. Prove that E lies on BD. (*Hint:* let the position vectors of A and B be **a** and **b** respectively. Write down the position vector of C and then of E. Find the vectors BE and BD.)

FLOW CHARTS

CONTENTS

▶ **Summary** 279

▶ **Flow charts** 279

▶ **Conventions** 279

▶ **Examination questions 27A** 281

▶ **Decision boxes** 283

▶ **Loops** 284

▶ **Examination questions 27B** 285

SUMMARY

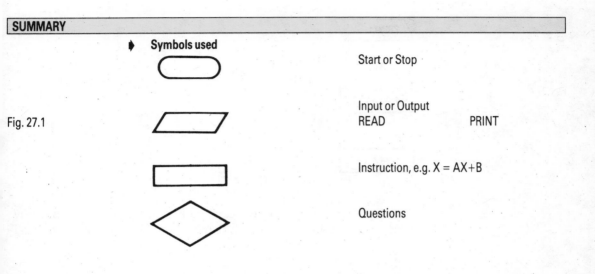

♦ **Symbols used**

Start or Stop

Fig. 27.1

Input or Output
READ   PRINT

Instruction, e.g. X = AX+B

Questions

FLOW CHARTS

Flow charts, sometimes called flow diagrams, are series of unambiguous instructions to carry out particular tasks, usually mathematical
tasks. They are useful in planning computer programs, for computers
need series of precise instructions or questions at each stage of their
working.

CONVENTIONS

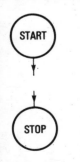

Fig. 27.2

Any series of instructions has to START and to STOP; these are
usually written in **circles** (sometimes ovals) at the beginning and end
of the flow chart (Fig. 27.2). There should be one initial operation, so
only one path should go from the START instruction, and only one
path lead to the STOP.

Any series of instructions must consist of unambiguous individual
instructions, and we may need to include some mathematical data.
Data are usually written in **parallelograms** (sometimes rectangular
boxes), as in Fig, 27.3, and calculations are always written in **rectangular boxes** (Fig. 27.4). Fig. 27.4(a) reads 'The new value of A is one
more than the old value of A' (sometimes the = is omitted and we

merely write $A{:}A{+}1$). Fig. 27.4(*b*) reads 'The new value of A is the product of the old value of A and the value of B.'

Fig. 27.3

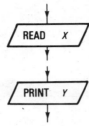

Fig. 27.4

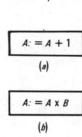

With these instructions we can work through some simple flow charts, remembering to record at each stage all the values we cal culate.

Specimen question Work through the flow chart in Fig. 27.5 using the following data. What numbers would be printed?
(*a*)   2, 4
(*b*)   3, 5
(*c*)   3, 3

Fig. 27.5

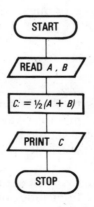

Answer
(*a*)   Here $A = 2$ and $B = 4$ so:

$$C = \tfrac{1}{2}(2{+}4) = 3$$

The number printed is 3.
(b) $A = 3$ and $B = 5$ so:

$$C = \tfrac{1}{2}(3+5) = 4$$

The number printed is 4.
(c) $A = 3$ and $B = 3$ so:

$$C = \tfrac{1}{2}(3+3) = 3$$

The number printed is 3.
Notice this flow chart calculates the mean of any two numbers put in.

EXAMINATION QUESTIONS 27A

Work through the following flow charts, recording each calculated number.

Fig. 27.6

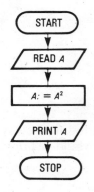

1   Fig. 27.6. Data: (a) 1; (b) 2; (c) 3.

Fig. 27.7

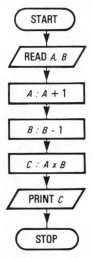

2   Fig. 27.7. Data: (a) 2, 3; (b) 3, 4; (c) 4, 4

Fig. 27.8

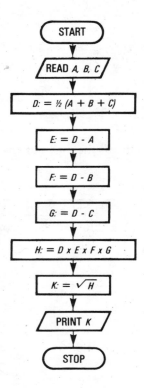

START

READ A, B, C

$D := \tfrac{1}{2}(A + B + C)$

$E := D - A$

$F := D - B$

$G := D - C$

$H := D \times E \times F \times G$

$K := \sqrt{H}$

PRINT K

STOP

3   Fig. 27.8. Data: 3, 4, 5.

Fig. 27.9

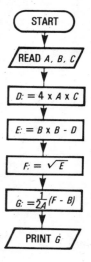

START

READ A, B, C

$D := 4 \times A \times C$

$E := B \times B - D$

$F := \sqrt{E}$

$G := \dfrac{1}{2A}(F - B)$

PRINT G

4   Fig. 27.9. Data: 6, −17, 12.

5   The flow chart in question **3** calculates the area of a triangle. Input the lengths of sides of other right-angled triangles and check that the flow chart obtains the area each time.

6   The flow chart in question **4** calculates one root of a quadratic equation. Make up a quadratic equation with known roots and work through the flow chart to see which root is obtained. Alter one rectangular box to produce a flow chart that gives the other root.

DECISION BOXES

In all flow charts except the very simplest we have a choice of operations after a decision has been made. The question requiring a decision is always written in a **diamond**. Sometimes we write the question mark and sometimes we do not, the fact that it is a question being implied by its being placed in a diamond box; for example, the two diamond boxes in Fig. 27.10 mean the same.

Fig. 27.10

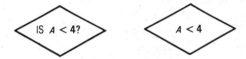

There must be only one path into a decision box, and only two paths out of it. Write NO or YES along the appropriate path.

Specimen question Work through the flow chart in Fig. 27.11 using the following data: (*a*) 5; (*b*) −6.

Fig. 27.11

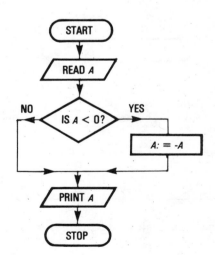

Answer This flow chart prints non-negative numbers, whatever the signs of the numbers input. Therefore 5 is printed as 5 and −6 is printed as 6.

Notice that the numbers printed are non-negative, not necessarily positive, as the question 'Is $A>0$?' has the answer NO when A is zero, and so 0 will then be printed.

LOOPS

After an appropriate answer to a question, we may wish to repeat the sequence, or part of the sequence, of calculations, perhaps to carry out a calculation a given number of times or to obtain a result to a given degree of accuracy. We use a **loop** for this.

Specimen question Work through the flow chart in Fig. 27.12, using 1 as your data.

Fig. 27.12

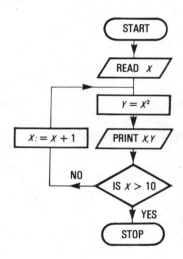

Answer The calculations of a flow chart are sometimes called the **trace**. Here, the trace would be printed in full, and reads as in Table 27.1.

Table 27.1

x	1	2	3	4	5	6	7	8	9	10
y	1	4	9	16	25	36	49	64	81	100

The flow chart calculates and prints the first 10 integers and their squares.

Work through the following flow charts.

Fig. 27.13

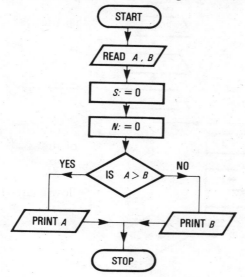

1 Fig. 27.13. Data: (*a*) 3, 4; (*b*) 5, 3; (*c*) 4, 4.

Fig. 27.14

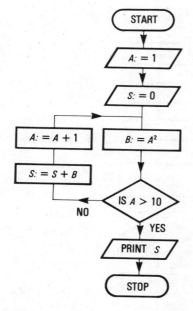

2 Fig. 27.14.

Fig. 27.15

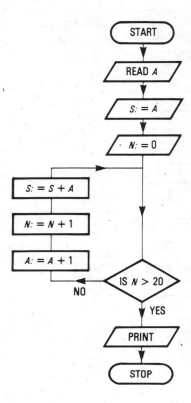

3 Fig. 27.15. Data: (*a*) $A = 1$; (*b*) $A = 5$.

Fig. 27.16

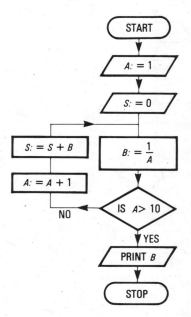

4 Fig. 27.16.

5   (*a*)   Amend the flow chart in Fig. 27.12 so that only the odd numbers and their squares are printed.

    (*b*)   Amend the flow chart in Fig. 27.12 so that only the even numbers from 2 to 10 and their squares are printed.

    (*c*)   Amend the flow chart in Fig. 27.12 so that only the squares of the first ten integers are printed, i.e. not the first ten integers as well.

6   (*a*)   Amend the flow chart in question 4 to give the sum:

$$\tfrac{1}{2}+\tfrac{1}{3}+\ldots\tfrac{1}{10}$$

    (*b*)   Amend the flow chart in question 4 to give the sum:

$$\tfrac{1}{3}+\tfrac{1}{5}+\tfrac{1}{7}+\ldots\tfrac{1}{21}$$

7   Floella's moped runs smoothly and is easy to start. Every time she slows down it stalls, the lights fade and the indicators stop flashing. Use the flow chart in Fig. 27.17 to find out what is wrong with it.

                                      [*SEG specimen question*]

Fig. 27.17

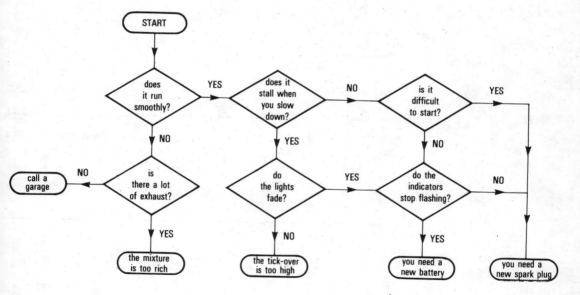

8   The flow diagram in Fig. 27.18 can be used to find the approximate square root of 20, after first choosing an appropriate whole number x as an estimate of $\sqrt{20}$.

     Start with $x = 4$ and make out a table like the one in Table 27.2 to show every stage in finding $\sqrt{20}$ to seven significant figures. Show all the figures on your calculator at each stage.

Fig. 27.18

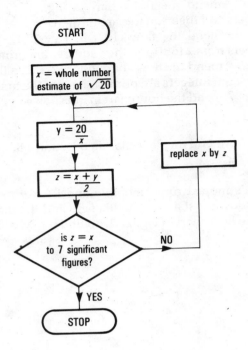

Table 27.2

x	y	z	Difference between x and z
4.0	5.0	4.5	0.5
4.5	4.4444444		
4.4722222			
etc.			

ITERATIVE METHODS TO SOLVE EQUATIONS

CONTENTS

▶ Finding a square root   291

▶ Examination questions 28   292

FINDING A SQUARE ROOT

We can use a method of repeated approximations to find, to any required degree of accuracy, the root of an equation. This can be illustrated by the following method for finding the square root of a positive number, N.

If x_n is a good approximation to the square root of N, it can be shown that:

$$x_{n+1} = \tfrac{1}{2}\left(x_n + \frac{N}{x_n}\right)$$

is a better approximation.

Suppose that we want to find $\sqrt{10}$, correct to five dp. We know that 3 is a good first approximation to $\sqrt{10}$, so take $x_0 = 3$. Then:

$$x_1 = \tfrac{1}{2}\left(3 + \frac{10}{3}\right)$$
$$= 3.166\ldots$$

Since it is unlikely that 3 is a very good approximation to $\sqrt{10}$, there is no advantage in taking x_1 with many places of decimals, so take:

$$x_1 = 3.1667$$

Then:

$$x_2 = \tfrac{1}{2}\left(3.1667 + \frac{10}{3.1667}\right)$$
$$= \tfrac{1}{2}(6.324\,56\ldots)$$
$$= 3.162\,28\ldots$$

Using a calculator, we do not need to write down each successive approximation as we obtain it, but can keep this in our working. Using this value of x_2, we have:

$$x_3 = \tfrac{1}{2}\left(3.162\,28\ldots + \frac{10}{3.162\,28\ldots}\right)$$
$$= 3.162\,277\ldots$$
$$= 3.162\,28, \text{ correct to five dp}$$

Since $x_3 = x_2 = 3.162\,28$ to five dp, we know that:

$$\sqrt{10} = 3.162\,28 \text{ to five dp}$$

This method can be used to solve a great variety of equations.

Specimen question Use the iteration:

$$x_{n+1} = 15 + \frac{1}{x_n}$$

to find one root of the equation:

$$x^2 - 15x - 1 = 0$$

correct to four dp.

Answer It does not matter in this case whether or not we can find a good starting approximation; any value of x other than 0 will converge rapidly to the root. Take:

$$x_0 = 1$$

Then:

$$x_1 = 15 + 1/1 = 16$$

Since $x_1 = 16$:

$$x_2 = 15 + 1/16$$
$$= 15.0625$$

Since $x_2 = 15.0625$:

$$x_3 = 15 + 1/15.0625$$
$$= 15.066\,39$$

Since $x_3 = 15.066\,39$:

$$x_4 = 15 + 1/15.066\,39$$
$$= 15.066\,37$$
$$x_5 = 15 + 1/15.066\,37$$
$$= 15.066\,37$$

Since $x_5 = x_4$ to four dp, the root is 15.0664, to four dp.

EXAMINATION QUESTIONS 28

1. Use the iteration given to find the square root, correct to five dp, of: (a) 5; (b) 50; (c) 0.7.
2. Starting with $x_0 = 1$, find, correct to five dp, the square root of 4.
3. Use the iteration:

    $$x_{n+1} = 7 - 4/x_n$$

    to find, correct to four dp, a root of:

    $$x^2 - 7x + 4 = 0$$

4. Use the iteration:

    $$x_{n+1} = 5 + 3/x_n$$

to find, correct to five dp, a root of:

$$x^2 - 5x - 3 = 0$$

5 A business requires containers (made from thin sheet metal), such that the internal measurements are related as shown in Fig. 28.1.

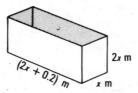

Fig. 28.1

(i) The internal volume of the container is $V\,\text{m}^3$.
(a) Calculate the value of V when $x = 0.6$.
(b) Write down a formula for V in terms of x.

(ii) The value of V is to be as close to 1 as possible.
(a) One possible re-arrangement of the equation obtained by putting $V = 1$ in the formula is:

$$x = \frac{1}{4x^2} - 0.1$$

Use an iterative method with this form of the equation to find the values of x_1, x_2 and x_3 when $x_0 = 0.6$.
(b) Show that the equation may also be rearranged as:

$$x = \frac{1}{2\sqrt{(x+0.1)}}$$

Use an iterative method with this x_0 form of the equation to find the values of x_1, x_2 and x_3 when $x_0 = 0.6$.
(c) State, correct to three significant figures, the required value of x.

[NEA specimen question]

ANSWERS

1 (a)   3, 7, 43   (b)   1, 9, 16
   (c)   1, 3, 15, 24   (d)   18, 24, 48
2 (a)   2×2×7×7; 14
   (b)   2×2×3×3×3×3; 18
   (c)   2×2×3×3×7×7; 42
3 (a)   2×2×2×2×3×3
   (b)   2×2×2×3×3×3
   (c)   3×3×7×7
   (d)   2×2×2×2×2×2×2×2×2
   Perfect squares: 144, 441. Perfect cubes: 216, 512
6 19.55 h; 23.05 h
7 22.40 h
8 −8°C
9 £28.40
10 Possible numbers are:
   (a)   5, next whole number.
   (b)   8, each being the sum of the two previous numbers.
   (c)   12, the sum of all previous numbers.
   (d)   11, increasing each time by 1 more than the previous increase.
   (e)   26, differences increasing by 2.
   (f)   30, second differences increasing by one each time.
11 $\frac{100}{101}$
12 5, 8; 1+2=3, etc.; 13;

$$x_{n+2} = x_{n+1}+x_n$$

1 $\frac{7}{17}, \frac{5}{13}, \frac{3}{13}$
2 (a) $\frac{7}{12}$ (b) $1\frac{1}{4}$ (c) $\frac{3}{4}$ (d) $\frac{13}{24}$
3 (a) $3\frac{5}{6}$ (b) $\frac{1}{12}$ (c) $\frac{5}{12}$ (d)   0
4 (a)   0.125   (b)   0.04   (c)   0.14   (d)   0.142
5 (a) $\frac{1}{4}$ (b) $\frac{6}{25}$ (c) $\frac{3}{8}$
6 (a)   20%   (b)   15%   (c)   14.8%
7 (a)   0.17   (b)   0.175   (c)   1.175
8 (a) $\frac{3}{20}$ (b) $\frac{11}{40}$ (c) $\frac{3}{8}$
9 820

10 Large; 1.1 g per penny.

EXAMINATION QUESTIONS 3A

1   (a) $2^4 \times 3^3$ (b) $2^6 \times 3^2$ (c) $2^6 \times 3^4$
    (d) $2^8 \times 3^5$ (e) $2^8 \times 3^6$ (f) $2^{18} \times 3^6$
    (g) $2^5 \times 3^5$ (h) 2^5 (i) $2^7 \times 3$
    (j) $2^9 \times 3$
2   (a) $2^2 \times 3$ (b) $2^4 \times 3$ (c) 2×3^4
    (d) 2×3^5
3   (a)   3, 2   (b)   5, 2

EXAMINATION QUESTIONS 3B

1   1/9
2   2
3   6
4   2
5   $\frac{1}{4}$
6   10
7   1
8   1/5
9   1
10   125

EXAMINATION QUESTIONS 3C

1   (a)   300   (b)   3700   (c)   30 700
    (d)   0.3   (e)   0.003
2   (a) 7.8×10^2 (b) 6.78×10^5 (c) 8×10^{-3}
    (d) 1×10^{-1}
3   (a) 6×10^5 (b) 1.5×10^{-1} (c) 1.5×10^5
    (d) 1.5×10
4   (a) 2×10^{-2} (b) 7.5×10^{-4}

EXAMINATION QUESTIONS 4A

1   (a)   240   (b)   255.5
2   (a)   4/3   (b)   1.515
3   (a)   2   (b)   1.985
4   (a)   105   (b)   113.05   (c)   6058
5   (a)   11.18   (b)   29.547972   (c)   1918.8975
6   £69.69

EXAMINATION QUESTIONS 4B

1   5300; 5400; 5400; 0.53; 0.50; 0.50.
2   5.35; 5.36; 5.36; 5.36; 0.55; 0.56; 0.51; 0.50.
3   (a)   48   (b)   72   (c)   0.3
     (d)   10

EXAMINATION QUESTIONS 5A

1   5:4:2
2   6:3:1
3   3:6:2
4   £1, £1.50, £2.50
5   £1000, £1500, £2000
6   £2.40, £3.60, £6.00

EXAMINATION QUESTIONS 5B

1   (a)   114   (b)   13.475   (c)   £666.90
     (d)   35.91 km
2   (a) $161   (b)   £21   (c)   6146 cm
3   (a)   25%   (b)   18.75%   (c)   5%

EXAMINATION QUESTIONS 5C

1   (a)   48.3   (b)   39.1   (c)   £41
     (d)   380 g
2   £418
3   £31.20
4   £3000; 125%; 25%
5   £3000
6   (a)   £1.92   (b)   £480
7    $\dfrac{100y}{x+y}$
8   £32; £34.56

EXAMINATION QUESTIONS 5D

1   128
2   800
3   (a)   1.5 min   (b)   6 min   (c)   180 seconds
4   (a)   £5.40   (b)   £20   (c)   £4
     (d)   70p
5   10 944
6   280

7 £2880
8 £2015.50

EXAMINATION QUESTIONS 6

1 £170
2 £9
3 £16
4 (a) £402 (b) £34 (c) £77
5 $3\frac{1}{2}\%$
6 3 months
7 £1600
8 6%
9 $12\frac{1}{2}\%$
10 £5400, £4752, £4052.16, £3296.33
11 £2336.26
12 (a) £129 (b) £104 (c) £1275
    (d) £980

EXAMINATION QUESTIONS 7

1 (a) 16.8 cm^2 (b) 28 cm^2
2 (a) 16 cm (b) 80 cm
3 (a) 1.5 km (b) 4 cm (c) 1 km^2
    (d) 16 cm^2
4 (a) 1:20 (b) 1:400 (c) 1:8000

EXAMINATION QUESTIONS 8A

These estimates are all approximations.
1 (a) 3 m (b) 800 km/h (c) 40 km/h
    (d) 40 km (e) 300 km
2 (a) 70 cm (b) 2 m by 1.2 m (c) 600 cm^3
    (d) 10 cm by 6 cm by 4 cm (e) 150 cm^3
3 (c)
4 (a)
5 (a), (c), (d)

EXAMINATION QUESTIONS 8B

1 (a) 500 g (b) 200 g (c) 80 kg
    (d) 120 kg (e) 150 tonnes

EXAMINATION QUESTIONS 9A

1. (a) 3.4, 3, 2   (b) 3, $2\frac{1}{2}$, 1   (c) $1\frac{5}{6}$, $1\frac{1}{2}$, 1
   (d) $2\frac{1}{2}$, $1\frac{1}{2}$, 0
2. (a) 3.4   (b) 0.34   (c) 23.4
   (d) 983.4
3. 3
4. 1

EXAMINATION QUESTIONS 9B

1. (a) 59.14   (b) (i) 62, (ii) 49, (iii) 390
2. (a) 33.25   (b) (i) 35, (ii) 14

EXAMINATION QUESTIONS 10A

1. (a) $\frac{4}{7}$ (b) $\frac{3}{7}$

2. $\dfrac{x}{x+y}$
3. (a) $\frac{1}{6}$ (b) $\frac{1}{3}$
4. $\frac{1}{2}$
5. $\frac{1}{7}$

EXAMINATION QUESTIONS 10B

1. (a) $\frac{7}{15}$ (b) $\frac{1}{6}$ (c) $\frac{1}{5}$
   (d) $\frac{7}{15}$ (e) $\frac{7}{15}$ (f) $\frac{7}{15}$; $\frac{7}{15}$
2. (a) $\frac{1}{25}$ (b) $\frac{8}{15}$ (c) $\frac{43}{75}$
   (d) $\frac{32}{75}$ (e) $\frac{449}{1125}$ (f) $\frac{1}{625}$
3. (a) 0.49   (b) 0.09   (c) 0.42
   (d) 0.1764   (e) 0.086

EXAMINATION QUESTIONS 11A

1. (a) $x+5$ (b) $x-3$ (c) $3x$
   (d) $2x+1$ (e) x^2-1
2. (a) $(a+b)$ cm   (b) $(2a+3b)$ cm   (c) ab cm^2
   (d) (a^2+b^2) cm   (e) $2(a+b+1)$ cm
3. (a) 9   (b) 32   (c) 144
   (d) 49   (e) 7   (f) 64
   (g) -12 (h) 0   (i) -48
   (j) 36   (k) 144   (l) 0

EXAMINATION QUESTIONS 11B

1. $2x(2-3y)$
2. $2h(2h-3)$
3. $4y(1-3y)$
4. $x^2(1+3x)$
5. $x^2(1+x^3)$
6. $x^2(1+x^4)$
7. $2a^2(1+3a-2b)$
8. $3x^2(y+1)$
9. $a^2(a^2+a+1)$
10. $4x^2(1+2x+3x^2+4x^3)$

EXAMINATION QUESTIONS 11C

1. $(x-y)(x+y)$
2. $(p-7q)(p+7q)$
3. $(5a-3b)(5a+3b)$
4. $2(s-3t)(s+3t)$
5. $4(1-3x)(1+3x)$
6. $7y(1-3y)(1+3y)$
7. $b(a-c)(a+c)$
8. $(x-1)(x+1)(x^2+1)$
9. $(a+b-c)(a-b+c)$
10. $\pi(x-y+z)(x-y-z)$
11. 2.2
12. 2
13. 4000
14. 31.4

EXAMINATION QUESTIONS 11D

1. $(x+1)(x+6)$
2. $(x-2)(x-3)$
3. $(y-3)(y+2)$
4. $(z-6)(z+1)$
5. $(x-6)(x+2)$
6. $(4x+1)(x-1)$
7. $(3x+2)(x-1)$
8. $(3y+2)(y-3)$
9. $(5+y)(1+y)$
10. $2(2x+5)(x-3)$

1 $(a+2)(a+x)$
2 $(x+2)(y+4)$
3 $(x+2)(x+y)$
4 $(x-y)(y-z)$
5 $(x+y)(x-y+1)$
6 $(x-y)(x+y+1)$
7 $(z+2)(z+1+a)$
8 $(y+5)(y+2+x)$

1 $c(a-b)(a+b)$
2 $c(a^2-b)$
3 $ac(a-b)$
4 $(a+b)(b+c)$
5 $(4a+1)(a-1)$
6 $(5+4t)(3-t)$
7 $(a-b)(2x-3y)$
8 $2(3x-5y)(3x+5y)$
9 $(x+2+10y)(x+2)$
10 $abc\,(a-1)(a+1)$

1 $7p$
2 9
3 155 at 30p, 55 at 50p
4 15 km
5 490 km

1 $\frac{4}{5}$
2 $\frac{7}{5}$
3 3
4 -3
5 $\frac{18}{5}$
6 3
7 -9
8 9
9 8
10 1

EXAMINATION QUESTIONS 12C

1 $x < 2$
2 $x < -\frac{2}{3}$
3 $x > \frac{2}{3}$
4 $x > 2$
5 $x > -7$
6 $x > -2$
7 $x > -2$
8 $x > 4$
9 $x > 56$
10 $x \leqslant 27$

EXAMINATION QUESTIONS 12D

1 $\frac{17}{13}, \frac{2}{13}$
2 $\frac{4}{11}, \frac{19}{11}$
3 $\frac{9}{2}, \frac{3}{4}$
4 $3, -4$
5 $120, 80$

EXAMINATION QUESTIONS 12E

1 -1 or 6
2 2 or 5
3 -2 or -3
4 0 or -5
5 0 or $-\frac{2}{3}$
6 -1 or $\frac{1}{3}$

EXAMINATION QUESTIONS 12F

1 -0.29 or -1.71
2 -0.22 or 2.22
3 -2.56 or 1.56
4 -2.64 or 1.14

EXAMINATION QUESTIONS 13A

1 (a) £2000 (b) £4900
2 12.00 h. Slow trains stop before they pass if Omnium less than 300 km from London.
3 (a) $11.20 (b) £8.57
4 (b) (i) $-1.25 \, \text{m/s}^2$, (ii) 68 m
5 (a) 6 min (b) 4 min (c) 2000 m (d) 2500 m

EXAMINATION QUESTIONS 13B

1 £1.40
2 (b)   100 mg   (c) $A = 170 - 10t$
   (d)   Between 6.30 am and 8.30 am on Sunday

EXAMINATION QUESTIONS 14A

1 0.67, 1.33
2 0.5, 2.5
3 0.75, 0.5
4 0.67, −0.67

EXAMINATION QUESTIONS 14B

1 (a)   −2.3 or 1.3   (b)   1.45 or −3.45
2 (a)   −0.78 or 1.28   (b) $y = \frac{1}{2}x + 2 - 1.2$ or 1.7
3 (a)   1.41; $1/x = x/2 \Rightarrow x^2 = 2$ (b) $y = \frac{1}{5}x \, 2.24$
4 (a)   −2.4 or 3.4   (b)   −2.55 or 3.55
5 (a) $0.23 \leqslant x \leqslant 1.43$ (b)   0.25 or 1
6 (a) $x < -2.2$, or $-0.2 < x < 2.4$ (b)   −2, −0.4 or 2.4

EXAMINATION QUESTIONS 14C

1 (a)   1   (b)   2, 4, 5   (c)   38
   (d)   36.5   (e)   36.125

EXAMINATION QUESTIONS 15B

1 (a) $x + y \leqslant 20$ (b) $x + 3y \leqslant 32$ (c) $x \geqslant 10$
   (d) $y \geqslant 4$ (e) $x \geqslant y + 2$ (f) $x \geqslant 2y$
   (g) $4x + 5y \leqslant 75$
2 (a) $x \geqslant 50$ (b) $y \leqslant 20$ (c) $x + y \leqslant 40$
   (d) $x + 2y \leqslant 200$ (e) $x \geqslant 3y$ (f) $x \geqslant y + 20$

EXAMINATION QUESTIONS 15C

1 8 of X, 10 of Y; 15 of X, none of Y
2 12 round, 15 square; 13 round, 14 square
3 $10x + 7y \leqslant 150$; $y > x$; $2y \leqslant 3x$; 8 dogs, 10 cats

EXAMINATION QUESTIONS 16A

1 (*a*)   Supplementary   (*b*)   Corresponding
   (*c*)   Supplementary   (*d*)   Alternate
3 36°, 72°, 72° or 45°, 45°, 90°
4 5.98 cm
5 75°

EXAMINATION QUESTIONS 16C

2 All are true

EXAMINATION QUESTIONS 17A

1 156°
2 20
3 16°

EXAMINATION QUESTIONS 17B

1 25 cm
2 17 cm, 12.7 cm
3 Less than

EXAMINATION QUESTIONS 17C

1 76°, 52°, 38°
2 80°, 50°, 140°, 40°, 140°
3 92° and 80°, 50° and 44°
4 35°, 30°, 65°

EXAMINATION QUESTIONS 17D

1 (*a*)   3:4   (*b*)   3:7
2 (*a*)   2:1   (*b*)   1:3   (*c*)   3:5
   (*d*)   5:4
4 (*a*)   6080 km (*b*)   12 160 km

EXAMINATION QUESTIONS 18

3 (a) 80°   (b) 100°
4 34°

EXAMINATION QUESTIONS 19

1 (a) Cube   (b) Cuboid   (c) Prism
   (d) Tetrahedron
3 (a) Cuboid   (b) Cylinder   (c) Half cylinder

EXAMINATION QUESTIONS 20A

1 (a) 0.3649   (b) 0.8536   (c) 0.8816
   (d) 0.7844   (e) 0.4746   (f) 3.0178
2 (a) 5.7°   (b) 11.5°   (c) 19.5°
   (d) 66.4°   (e) 60°   (f) 48.2°
   (g) 35°   (h) 38.7°   (i) 53.1°
3 (a) 6.04 cm, 5.25 cm   (b) 54.3°, 4.66 cm
   (c) 33.6°, 6.63 cm   (d) 41.2°, 10.6 cm

EXAMINATION QUESTIONS 20B

1 (a) 4.7 cm   (b) 7.31 cm   (c) 8.14 cm
   (d) 13.7 cm
2 (a) 16.9°   (b) 7.8°
3 7.82 km, 052°
4 12.9°
5 1.37 km, 2.92 km

EXAMINATION QUESTIONS 21A

1 72°, 8.89, 6.49
2 46.9°, 93.1°, 11.5 cm; 6.9°, 1.4 cm
3 60°, 38°, 82°
4 10.4 cm, 47°, 53°

EXAMINATION QUESTIONS 21B

1 3800 km
2 2910 km
3 15 640 km, 18 900 km

EXAMINATION QUESTIONS 21C

1   1.03 m
2   56°, 64°
3   14°

EXAMINATION QUESTIONS 22

1   (e)   5   (f)   0
2   45°, 45°, 90°

EXAMINATION QUESTIONS 23

1   (a)   2   (b)   1   (c) $1\frac{1}{2}$
    (d)   0   (e)   2   (f)   1

2   $f^{-1}:y \mapsto y+3;\ g^{-1}:y \mapsto \dfrac{2}{y};\ (fg)^{-1}:y \mapsto \dfrac{2}{y+3}$

EXAMINATION QUESTIONS 24A

1   (a) $\begin{pmatrix} 5 & -1 \\ 9 & 4 \end{pmatrix}$ (b) $\begin{pmatrix} -4 & -1 \\ -6 & 1 \end{pmatrix}$ (c) $\begin{pmatrix} 12 & -3 \\ 22 & 11 \end{pmatrix}$

    (d) $\begin{pmatrix} 1 & -1 \\ 27 & 3 \end{pmatrix}$ (e) $\begin{pmatrix} 6 & -3 \\ 14 & -2 \end{pmatrix}$ (f) $\begin{pmatrix} 1 \\ 17 \end{pmatrix}$

    (g) $\begin{pmatrix} 6 \\ 13 \end{pmatrix}$ (h) $(0\ \ -5)$ (i) $(1\ \ -1)$

    (j) $\begin{pmatrix} 4 & -2 \\ 6 & -3 \end{pmatrix}$ (k) (1) (l) $\begin{pmatrix} 0 & -5 \\ 20 & 5 \end{pmatrix}$

2   −12, 16
3   $-\frac{3}{2}$, −3
4   4, −8
6   $\begin{pmatrix} 566 \\ 922 \\ 1064 \\ 708 \\ 1208 \end{pmatrix}$ cost of postage each day; (116, 170), number of letters of each class posted that week; (4468), cost in pence of mail that week

7   $\begin{pmatrix} 1 & 1 & 0 & 0 \\ 1 & 0 & 1 & 0 \\ 0 & 1 & 1 & 1 \end{pmatrix}; \begin{pmatrix} 3 & 1 & 2 & 0 \\ 1 & 3 & 4 & 3 \end{pmatrix}$; there are two routes from A to Q

8   $\begin{pmatrix} 57 \\ 0 \end{pmatrix}; \begin{pmatrix} 69 \\ 0 \end{pmatrix}$

EXAMINATION QUESTIONS 24B

1 (a) $\quad$ 3 $\qquad$ (b) $\quad$ 13 $\qquad$ (c) $\quad$ 1
$\quad$ (d) $\quad$ -1
2 (a) and (b)

3 (a) $\begin{pmatrix} \frac{3}{2} & -\frac{1}{2} \\ -2 & 1 \end{pmatrix}$ $\quad$ (b) $\begin{pmatrix} 2 & -1 \\ -5 & 3 \end{pmatrix}$ $\quad$ (c) $\begin{pmatrix} \frac{2}{11} & \frac{1}{11} \\ -\frac{5}{11} & \frac{3}{11} \end{pmatrix}$

$\quad$ (d) $\begin{pmatrix} \frac{1}{3} & -\frac{2}{3} \\ \frac{1}{12} & \frac{1}{3} \end{pmatrix}$ $\quad$ (e) $\begin{pmatrix} \frac{1}{2} & 0 \\ 0 & \frac{1}{2} \end{pmatrix}$ $\quad$ (f) $\begin{pmatrix} 0 & -1 \\ -1 & 2 \end{pmatrix}$

4 $3, 2$
5 $\frac{3}{5}, \frac{2}{5}$
6 (a) $\quad$ $3.2, -1.4$ $\qquad$ (b) $\quad$ $-0.2, 1.4$ $\qquad$ (c) $\quad$ $0.3, -0.1$
7 $2, -1$
8 (a) $\quad$ $2, -1$ $\qquad$ (b) $\quad$ $-\frac{1}{7}, -\frac{4}{7}$ $\qquad$ (c) $\quad$ $\frac{2}{7}, \frac{1}{7}$

EXAMINATION QUESTIONS 25

1 (a) $\quad$ (v) $\qquad$ (b) $\quad$ (ii)
2 (ii)
3 Reflection of transformation made by **S** in $y = x$.
4 Rotation about origin through $\tan^{-1}\left(\frac{4}{3}\right)$, clockwise sense.
5 Rotation about origin through 90°, clockwise sense. Shear parallel to x-axis.

EXAMINATION QUESTIONS 26A

1 (a) $\begin{pmatrix} 2 \\ 3 \end{pmatrix}$ $\quad$ (b) $\begin{pmatrix} 3 \\ 5 \end{pmatrix}$ $\quad$ (c) $\begin{pmatrix} -1 \\ -2 \end{pmatrix}$

$\quad$ (d) $\begin{pmatrix} 1 \\ 2 \end{pmatrix}$ $\quad$ (e) $\begin{pmatrix} 1 \\ -3 \end{pmatrix}$

2 (a) $\quad$ $2\sqrt{2}, 45°$ $\qquad$ (b) $\quad$ $3\sqrt{2}, -45°$ $\qquad$ (c) $\quad$ $\sqrt{2}, 135°$
$\quad$ (d) $\quad$ $2\sqrt{2}, -135°$
3 (a) $\quad$ $\sqrt{26}$ $\qquad$ (b) $\quad$ $\sqrt{5}$ $\qquad$ (c) $\quad$ $\sqrt{73}$
$\quad$ (d) $\quad$ 2 $\qquad$ (e) $\quad$ $\sqrt{82}$
4 $\frac{1}{2}$
5 $-\frac{1}{2}$
6 $5, 7$

EXAMINATION QUESTIONS 26B

1	(a)	1	(b)	1.73
2	(a)	75°	(b)	15°
3	1.81, 25°			
4	106°			
5	(a)	2.65	(b)	41°

EXAMINATION QUESTIONS 26C

1 $\overrightarrow{BA} = \mathbf{a} - \mathbf{b}$

2 1:3

4 $\begin{pmatrix} 5 \\ 7 \end{pmatrix}$

EXAMINATION QUESTIONS 27A

1	(a)	1	(b)	4	(c)	9
2	(a)	6	(b)	12	(c)	15
3	6					
4	3/2					

6 $G := -\dfrac{1}{2A}(F+B)$

EXAMINATION QUESTIONS 27B

1	(a)	4	(b)	5	(c)	4
2	385					
3	(a)	210	(b)	315		

4 $2.928968\ldots, 2\frac{2341}{2520}$

5	(a)	$x := x+2$	(b)	Data: 2, $x := x+2$
	(c)	PRINT y		
6	(a)	$A := 2$	(b)	$A := 3$, $A := A+2$, IS $A > 21$.

7 New battery needed.

8 4.472136, 4.472136, 4.472136, 0.000000

1 (a)   2.236 07   (b)   7.071 07   (c)   0.836 67

2 2.000 00

3 6.3723

4 5.541 38

5 (i)   (a) $10.08\,m^3$ (b) $V = 4x^2(x+0.1)$

    (ii)   (a)   0.594, 0.607, 0.577   (b)   0.5976, 0.5986, 0.5982

           (c)   0.598